BATTLEFIELD
MEDICS

BATTLEFIELD MEDICS

HOW WARFARE CHANGED THE HISTORY OF MEDICINE

MARTIN KING

This edition published in 2021 by Arcturus Publishing Limited
26/27 Bickels Yard, 151–153 Bermondsey Street,
London SE1 3HA

AD007755UK

Printed in the UK

FSC
www.fsc.org

MIX
Paper from
responsible sources
FSC® C018072

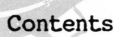

Contents

Foreword

'These things we do so that others may live,' so states the combat medic's creed. I've departed the relative safety of a combat outpost, travelled a treacherous road or penetrated enemy infested areas by helicopter more times than I can remember. I've done this every time without a full complement of people and equipment. It's the way of the infantry. You never have everything you need. I may have been missing a rifleman or two, or even a key piece of combat gear, but I was never missing my medic. Never. Their names I've long since forgotten, probably because we called them all 'doc', but their faces are seared in my mind forever. I can see them today in their combat gear, determined looks on their faces, medical bags strung tightly across their back, ready for that infamous call: 'medic!'

It is the solemn duty of a combat commander to accomplish the mission and bring his or her people home alive. We take this very seriously, especially the latter, and we accomplish this in large part through a detailed medical treatment and evacuation plan and network which saves lives from the point of injury backwards. At the centre of this is the medic.

There is little comfort in battle. Loaded with heavy, uncomfortable body armour, water, ammunition and bulky weapons, engaged in physical activity akin to intense cross-fit training, a soldier finds little comfort. Land forces are the most vulnerable of military service members, exposed to the wrath of enemy weapons and improvised explosive devices (IEDs). Any brief period of respite from the rigours of this environment is a welcome moment for a soldier; catching a breath behind protective cover, a lull in the fighting, the surrender of a foe or the arrival of a medic. Especially the arrival of a medic.

There is nothing quite so powerful, so comforting, so healing than human connection. We long for this from the moment of our birth and into our adulthood. This is especially true on the battlefield. Aside from their battle buddy, a medic or nurse is that human connection soldiers desire. From the terrifying point of injury to the stabilizing, healing period in a hospital, it is our medics and nurses, not our captains, sergeants or even doctors who deliver this unwavering, loving care.

It's no accident that we've dubbed our medics 'Angels of the Battlefield'. When something profoundly positive happens in our lives, many of us look upward in gratitude to an angel we believe helped us, guided us or protected us. The same is true in war. A combat injury takes us back to our childhood when we were powerless, requiring the protection and care of a parent. In war, injured, we lay flat on the scorched earth of a battlefield or the white angelic comfort of a hospital bed, immobilized by our injuries, powerless, looking for that same protection and care. When we look up this time, we see a real angel. A medic.

Riflemen have it tough on the battlefield, medics have it tougher. Riflemen must close with and destroy an enemy often against great odds manoeuvring directly into enemy fire. Medics fight alongside riflemen yet must perform their life-saving duties, often under fire, sacrificing their own safety and wellbeing for that of another. In an instant they transition from rifleman to medic. Precision with a weapon quickly turns into precision with their hands and the tools of their life-saving trade.

In this book, you'll be taken on a journey of medical advancements in technology and forward medical evacuation saving an increasing number of lives. The cockpits of modern aircraft and the dashboards and communications equipment of motorized infantry formations have become increasingly technologically advanced. Combat medical care is no exception. Amidst these advancements, one thing remains constant. That is the skill and bravery of a medic providing point-of-injury care. Through technological growth and change, the need for one human to come to the aid of another will most certainly transcend the evolution of warfare.

Everyone prays for the end of war altogether, especially those who don the military uniform of their country. Indeed, no person reviles war more than one who must fight it. As long as humans inhabit the earth, war is likely to exist. And despite advancements in stand-off weaponry, unmanned ground and aerial platforms and other technological advancements, humans will continue to wage war. Brave warriors will be required to seize and hold terrain, capture prisoners, train indigenous forces and solve rural societal issues which fuel insurgencies. Unfortunately, years from now, in some future war on a distant battlefield, a soldier is sure to be injured from an enemy attack. And while that soldier will be equipped with more advanced protective equipment and even monitoring devices to quickly determine injury, they will still look upward. They will still revert to their childhood yearning for that protection and loving care. And when they look up on this future battlefield, they will yearn to see that person everyone knows. Doc. A person who seeks neither reward nor honour for their efforts. A person who treats friend and enemy with the same traditions as those who have gone before. They will see a combat medic. They will see an angel.

Colonel Robert Campbell (retired),
1st Brigade Combat Team, 101st Airborne Division, US Army.

Preface

I've been around people in the medical profession for most of my life. My mother was a nurse, my wife is a nurse and my daughter and one of my sisters worked in psychiatry. They are among the finest and most resilient people I have ever known. They are also drastically underpaid for the work they do. One of the nurses who most impacted my life began her career in a general hospital. Her name was Augusta Chiwy, the subject of my book *Searching for Augusta* and the multiple Emmy Award-winning documentary of the same name.

While researching Augusta's story I developed a fresh appreciation and respect for all combat medical personnel. It inspired me to look deeper into the subject. Another incentive that inspired this volume was a visit to the excellent Jacob Weikert farm at Gettysburg. The owners told me the story of a young extemporized nurse called Tillie Pierce, and the terrible conditions she laboured under during and after the battle. I'd never heard about her and many other illustrious names. Hopefully, this volume will go some way to amending this deficit.

Most military historians tend to focus on the campaigns, generals and individuals who participated in or orchestrated the fighting. It goes with the turf, but war is a multi-faceted experience; it's about saving life as well as taking it. Contemporary movies such as *Hacksaw Ridge* and old TV series such as *M.A.S.H.* highlighted the roles played by army medics in various deadly warzones. They did a great job of drawing attention to the incredible work done by these individuals. I even recall attempting to join a MASH unit when I was in my late teens because the TV show and the movie had such a profound effect on my young life. Sadly, lacking the most basic concept of self-discipline, I realized early on I wasn't cut out for it at any level. Consequently, I never made it beyond the Sea Cadets. Even there I'd hear stories of how the Royal Navy used lemons and limes to combat the rampant scurvy that frequently whittled down the ships' crews on long voyages. One petty officer spoke with great reverence about the role of Royal Navy surgeons during the Napoleonic Wars. Most of these naval physicians had medical degrees and were all fully paid-up members of the elite College of Physicians.

Hence the seeds of my interest were sown many decades ago. This book is the culmination of my fascination with military medical services. It isn't a morbid or bloodthirsty obsession, merely a token of my respect and passion for the chosen subject. Even though Augusta Chiwy encouraged me greatly, the interest was to some extent already there; she was just the proverbial spark. She was my 'Angel' of Bastogne but, as you will discover, there were other angels and other battles. To the commanders of armies they were just there to repair the wounded, but to those afflicted and dying they really were angels. It is my profound hope that the stories contained in this volume will inspire and nurture a greater love and a greater appreciation of those who dared to venture into the dominions of hell to save lives.

Martin King,
2021

Introduction

For centuries, while the dust was still clearing and the battle was still raging, these remarkable men and women have often put themselves in harm's way to attend the wounded and dying. From the Peloponnesian Wars to the hills and mountains of Afghanistan, they have braved slings and arrows, bombs and bullets to do their job. Even the ancient Egyptians had a nominal concept of basic battlefield medicinal practices that combined the application of soothing herbs with dubious celestial requirements designed for one purpose, to patch up the wounded as best they could and get them fighting again. The Greeks expanded on the idea considerably and the Roman legions even employed organized medical units in their armies.

During the Dark Ages while the Vikings were ravaging the shores of Britannia, most of the invaluable knowledge collected by the Egyptians, Greeks and Romans had been lost to posterity. Many centuries would pass before army commanders came to realize the potential benefits of caring for, and even healing, the casualties of war.

These days a Red Cross or Red Crescent on armbands or helmets usually distinguishes frontline medical personnel from other military crew, but this wasn't always the case. The men and women who responded to the cry of 'Medic!' were a remarkable collective indeed, unimpeded by race or ethnicity, and equally undefined by nationality or gender they proved on innumerable occasions that care has no colour and courage has no creed. These pages are a small tribute to some truly exceptional human beings.

From Ramses and Julius Caesar to Napoleon and Patton, it was overtly apparent how integral trained medical staff was to any serious military operation, but it took a long time for the notion to register. Once it was established that a wounded soldier could be patched up and sent back to the front, those encumbered by intransigent ideologies began to reassess the vital importance of the invaluable service that medical personnel could provide. This led to the establishment of real frontline medical services, but it was a tortuously painful road. As this volume progresses you will read first-hand accounts from veterans of various wars and conflicts.

Applying medical innovations was one thing, but other important elements that medical staff provided could be neither learned nor taught. Care, courage and compassion is unquantifiable but equally important to the wounded. The expression 'to go above and beyond' is an often-used phrase that is applied when describing deeds of heroism, but here were a group of people who did precisely that at almost every conceivable juncture. They would endure the same deprivations and hardships as those who did the fighting and frequently took the same risks without receiving the same accolades or credit. Now it's time to tell their stories.

PART ONE

THOSE HEALING HANDS

CHAPTER ONE

WHERE IT ALL BEGAN

The Egyptians believed that the application of successful wound treatments demanded prescribing both observable and supernatural elements. For this purpose, they would inevitably respect practical physical remedies but be prepared to throw in the odd magic spell or spontaneous dance routine for added efficacy. Their medicine also relied on the combined power of incantations along with herbal concoctions to hopefully achieve a desired result. The right words could invalidate or deflect malicious forces, and the use of amulets or materials that had been in contact with powerful talismans were also expected to render a salutary effect. This was often to the detriment of the afflicted soldier whose primary considerations rarely exceeded, 'Do something quick, this stings you know?'

As Egyptian troops ventured forth into battle they often wore an amulet for protection that depicted the gruesome image of the Egyptian god Bes. This was thought to deter malevolent gods or the hostile spirits of the dead. In the event of Bes being preoccupied with other matters the image was augmented with a massive shield and a pair of sturdy legs that, as the situation evolved, could switch direction at any given moment. Ancient Egyptians didn't rely entirely on supernatural remedies when coping with physical traumas. One papyrus written during a period of

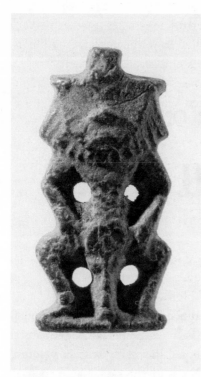

Amulet of Egyptian god Bes, c.1550–1295BC. One of the many gods the ancient Egyptians invoked to cure their wounded.

internecine struggle and warfare refers to a physician actively treating battle casualties.

It describes in detail the types of weapon that would have inflicted the wounds that were used by both Egyptian soldiers and their enemies in combat. The physical treatments and prescriptions involved a compendium of substances compiled over the course of millennia. Surgery was exceedingly rare, and dissection was definitely not considered a feasible option. Physicians of the day employed a vast pharmacopoeia of natural substances such as honey and pomegranate juice, a powerful astringent. The water lily plant that was applied to wounds and abrasions has been proven to contain analgesic properties and may also have been ingested on occasion for that purpose. Residues discovered in distinctive tall-necked vessels that may have been imported from Asia Minor suggest that Egyptian physicians were acquainted with the anaesthetic properties of opium. All physicians were meticulously trained and required to become skilled practitioners of physical and supernatural medicine. Some centuries later the Greeks would also invoke their gods for numerous purposes, but tended to rely on more practical solutions when treating the wounded.

Hippocrates, the renowned Greek physician of the Age of Pericles, is credited with the famous oath, 'He who desires to practise surgery must go to war.' What he implied was that only during warfare could a physician truly learn his art, closing wounds, treating infection, and learning the intricacies of human anatomy. One passage from Homer's *Iliad* states: 'A physician is worth more than several other men put together, for he can cut out arrows and spread healing herbs.' This takes into account of course that most wounds would have resulted from the implementation of the hacking, stabbing or slashing practices employed by ancient armies. Although their anaesthetic value may have been questionable some of the 'healing herbs' applied to the afflicted areas could indeed be quite efficacious.

The ancient Greek term for the person who cared for the wounded was '*iatros*', apparently derived from an old Ionian word meaning 'extractor of arrows'. The Greeks effectively cleansed wounds with a concoction assembled from wine and vinegar. Greek wine contained polyphones, which are bactericides 33 times more powerful than the phenols Joseph Lister used in 1865.

It's generally known that Alexander the Great's army used tourniquets made of brass and leather to staunch wounds. However, they didn't have the knowledge to permanently arrest the bleeding once a tourniquet was removed. Alexander openly acknowledged the benefits of having trained physicians to accompany his armies and they operated in situations not completely alien to contemporary medical staff. He only had seven overworked physicians to tend an army of around 40,000. His experience would inspire the Roman Army to incorporate a highly organized and efficient military medical service as a standard addition to all its conquering legions.

When the Roman armies began expanding to support the imperial ambitions of their emperor, they developed something that resembled a distinct system of military medicine. Once the Roman Army had defeated the Greeks and forced them to renounce their independence, the Roman medical service improved on the Greek version by incorporating trained physicians and establishing field hospitals to tend their wounded. Plato had been correct when he wrote, 'all the good things of the conquered pass into the hands of the conquerors'.

The Roman author Vegetius wrote that the Roman Army should be 'preserved' by providing 'a good, clean water supply, taking seasonal considerations into account, the use of medicine, and exercise for the troops'. He emphasized that commanders should not march the troops in baking sun or in freezing weather, and that clean drinking water was an imperative at all times. He was among the first to state categorically that sick soldiers should be 'brought back to health by suitable food and cured by the skills of doctors'. Each doctor attached to the army would be required to successfully pass through the appropriate school before being allowed to unleash his talent on the legionaries. Battlefield medicine was exclusively a male domain at that time and its application in the Roman Army was remarkably advanced even by contemporary standards. It far exceeded the medical knowledge of the medieval period.

A Roman medical officer was known as the *medicus*. This trained doctor was usually in charge of Greek, or Greek-trained medical personnel known as the 'medici'. The exact rank and hierarchic position of the medici within the army has never been conclusively ascertained. They were usually employed in the service of Rome after being captured as prisoners of war.

Wounded Roman soldiers would receive initial treatment by medics called *capasarii*, who carried boxes of bandages. Later Roman Army surgeons were usually given the rank of *magister* or 'master'. Records show that medical supplies and carriages for bearing the wounded were strategically placed in the middle of marching columns.

Archaeological discoveries in the town of Xanten (known as Vetera to the Romans) in Germany unearthed what is assumed by many to be a Roman hospital (Valetudinarium) complete with wards, rooms full of medical instruments, surgical suites, convalescence rooms, and possibly mortuaries. These hospitals were originally built to serve the military.

Under the auspices of the Roman general and statesman Gaius Marius, the Roman Army became the best trained and most disciplined force the known world had ever witnessed, and their military medical services became the envy of all opposing armies.

In the seventh book of Pliny's *Natural History*, published in AD77, the author refers to Marcus Sergius Silus Ferrous, Roman general and politician who lived from *c*.240–187BC and fought during the Punic and Epirote Wars. According to Pliny, this Roman general was one of the first soldiers to wear a prosthetic limb, his right hand having been sliced off in a sword fight. Not only did the general live to tell the tale, he actively participated in many ensuing battles – whereupon he sustained a further 23 separate injuries to his extremities.

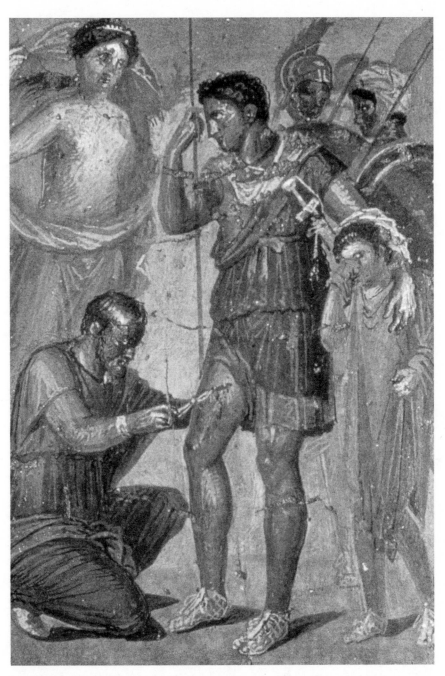

A Roman fresco of a medicus *treating the battlefield wounds sustained by Aeneas, the legendary Trojan hero.*

He managed to maintain his prowess in battle by fashioning a prosthetic iron hand capable of holding a shield and splitting enemy skulls with remarkable dexterity. His enemies were frequently reduced to awestruck silence as he stabbed, gouged and slashed away to great effect. Twice taken prisoner by Hannibal's Carthaginians, he managed to escape on both occasions. After military service he ventured into politics, where he served as a Roman praetor. A number of his colleagues attempted to prevent the former general from participating in public ceremonies because of his perceived 'deformity'. Nevertheless, Sergius confounded his detractors, which to some extent made him the world's first advocate for the rights of veteran amputees.

In the Roman Army the person who would have initially tended the general would have been the *medicus*, using the instruments at their disposal for the treatment of wounds. Their primary use would have been for the extraction of arrowheads and small stones fired by slings, but there were various other instruments that were remarkably similar to those employed by surgeons of the nineteenth and early twentieth centuries. Roman surgeons used forceps, scalpels, tourniquets, ear scoops, catheters and even arterial clamps. They wouldn't have had any knowledge of bacterial infections, but had some concept of hygiene because they usually took the precaution of boiling instruments before and after every procedure.

The *medicus* also had sedatives and painkillers at their disposal to enhance their bedside manner, including opium and henbane seeds, which contained scopolamine, also known as hyoscine, which is used to treat motion sickness and post-operative nausea and vomiting.

Wounded Roman soldiers were treated with acetum, a concoction made from vinegar which proved a feasible antiseptic but which was by all accounts excruciatingly painful when applied to wounds. It took four or five *capasarii* to restrain a patient when it was used, but as an antiseptic it was known to prevent some infections and even prevent superficial wounds from becoming fatal.

Sadly, many of these Greek and Roman remedies were lost by the Middle Ages, only to be recovered in the modern era.

Historians agree that the quality and effectiveness of Roman military medicine was not surpassed until at least the seventeenth and eighteenth centuries. The care given to a Roman soldier was in fact almost equivalent to that received by a soldier in World War I.

The word 'nurse' is derived from the Latin word *nutrire*, meaning to suckle, and originally may have referred to a maternity nurse. It wasn't until the late sixteenth century that the word 'nurse' obtained its contemporary meaning as someone who provides care and comfort for the infirm.

It's said that the world's first nursing school was founded in India about 250BC. Writings from the time indicate that only men were considered 'pure' enough to become nurses. This was also the case in ancient Rome, where the '*nosocomi*' were men who provided nursing care. The term 'nosocomial', meaning 'hospital acquired', stems from the late Latin word for hospital, *nosocomium*. Women were overlooked again in AD300, when another group of men known as the Parabolani started a hospital providing voluntary nursing care and funeral services during a plague epidemic in Alexandria, during the episcopate of Dionysius the Great. The name Parabolani is derived from the Latin meaning 'to disregard', as the men of this fraternal organization deliberately exposed themselves to contagious diseases. When the Roman Empire became the Byzantine Empire, further medical innovations occurred with the establishment of two hospitals within the great city of Constantinople, housing both male and female nurses. They were known as '*hypourgoi*' and helped to advance nursing on a global scale.

However, it's important to note that nursing only became much more common in Europe during the Middle Ages, due primarily to its spread by the all-powerful Catholic Church.

It was St Benedict, born around 480 in Norcia, in modern Italy, who founded the Benedictine monks' nursing order, and here the parameters become slightly blurred because his twin sister St Scholastica went on to establish a similar monastic-based community of women. What little we know about St Benedict was written about a generation later in the *Dialogues of Gregory the Great*, by Pope Gregory I, the man who established the medieval papacy.

When Charlemagne became Holy Roman Emperor in 800 he undertook to restore and equip the hospitals of his domain with all of the latest medical equipment. He also demanded that hospitals be attached to every cathedral and monastery within Europe, which helped to stimulate demand for more nurses. Monasteries began siting hospitals within their premises, as well as building separate infirmaries, with the stipulation that their services were only available to the genuinely pious. Heathens and worshippers of other religions were not welcome.

Military, religious and lay orders of men including the Knights Hospitallers, the Teutonic Knights, the Knights of St Lazarus and the Hospital Brothers of St Anthony provided nursing care during the Middle Ages. Then there were the Alexians, informal groups of laymen who provided nursing care for the poor in the twelfth century.

CHAPTER TWO

THE PAINFUL MIDDLE AGES

After the fall of the Roman Empire, western Europe receded dramatically from the well-ordered structure and discipline of the Classical Era and replaced it with what became known as feudalism. The onset of the feudal period began around the ninth century in western and central Europe. In time it disseminated to other parts of the Continent, finally grinding to a stuttering halt in the fifteenth century in western Europe, although elements of feudalism continued for considerably longer in eastern Europe.

This system of enforced subjugation was based on strict hierarchies with each group having obligations and expectations from the groups above and below them. Under this despised system, everyone but the king had a ruling lord above him to whom he owed loyalty, fealty and service in exchange for land and protection. A few peasants retained their liberty, but they were in the minority because most became serfs, slaves to the lord of the manor. They were required to stay on the land and pay extortionately high rents to the lord. Adding insult to injury, in times of war or armed conflict the menfolk were expected to bear arms and serve the feudal lord unquestioningly. Existing records offer extensive accounts of the often-nefarious means feudal kings used to raise their armies. Detailed inventories of feudal obligations were maintained to calculate the total number of knights that might be pressed into service when required.

There is little reference in these records concerning the treatment of wounded soldiers. The general assumption is that it depended largely on the generosity or parsimony of the respective feudal lord to care for the knights and foot soldiers in his service and, more often than not, it fell to the monasteries to care for disabled soldiers who had signed on to fight for wages. The only hope for these unfortunate peasants depended solely on their obedient adherence to devout Christianity and the conviction, imposed or otherwise, that life in heaven would be considerably better than life on Earth.

While resident on the manor most people endured a desultory existence, usually centred around the castle, church, village and surrounding farmland. These manors were usually quite isolated, and only rarely enlivened by visits from peddlers, pilgrims on their way to the Holy Land, or soldiers from other fiefdoms. The care a soldier received at this troubled time depended entirely on the status of that individual. Even though many feudal lords were ignorant of the values of genuine altruism, they cared for their knights, while monasteries were encumbered with looking after the fiscally challenged ordinary foot soldier, or pitchfork-wielding peasant.

During medieval times, treatment of wounded soldiers on and off the battlefield often fell to the clergy, where the imposition of stringent religious doctrine frequently impeded the quality of care received. The sharp division of the medical profession into physicians and surgeons can be traced back to the twelfth century, when the Catholic Church officially forbade the clergy to shed blood under any circumstance. Although this proved problematic to the extraction of arrowheads or crossbow bolts, priests and monks continued, often surreptitiously, to practise medicine. Actual surgery, however, was allocated to the dubious talents of their former lay assistants, whose primary duty comprised shaving the monks' heads with sharp blades. This development hailed the advent of the lower-status profession of the 'barber-surgeon', of which more later.

Sometime around 1048, Italian merchants in Amalfi founded an organization that became known as the Knights Hospitaller. These merchants established the order primarily to provide medical care and a safe haven for sick, injured and poverty-stricken pilgrims venturing to Jerusalem and the Holy Land. Monks and other quasi-religious or military orders that accompanied the Crusaders were usually the ones organizing this service. All willingly and fervently responded to the call 'Deus vult' (God wills it).

Crusading forces were comprised from a diverse demographic, the result of the broad appeal of Urban II's papal bull to launch the First Crusade in 1095. The Crusader knights were accompanied by a veritable plethora of craftsmen. There were farriers and armourers, along with huntsmen to care for the knights' hawks and dogs, but there was little or no provision for personal hygiene or medical needs.

The Crusaders' complete disregard for personal hygiene proved to be one of the greatest affronts to Arab sensibilities in the Holy Land. The Syrian writer Usama ibn Munqidh in his volume *The Book of Instruction* openly disdained the Crusaders' negligible practices when he noted that, 'In the first, the Franks simply lopped off a knight's mildly infected leg with an axe; in the second, they carved a cross into an ill woman's skull before rubbing it with salt. Both patients died on the spot, at which point the Arab doctor asked, "Do you need anything else from me?" "No," they said. And so I left, having learned about their medicine things I had never known before.'

This lack of personal hygiene among the Crusaders may well have contributed to the significantly large number of them who perished in the plague following the eight-month siege of Antioch in 1098.

In a later Crusade Richard I's generosity and mercy to the poor, providing transport for them and saving many lives in the process, provided the catalyst for his reputation as a Crusader leader. Frederick Barbarossa equally displayed an altruistic streak when he accepted responsibility for the health of his troops by providing specially made carts to transport the sick, 'so that the destitute crowd of languishing people should not perish on the way'. These could have in effect been the first ambulances.

There were surgeons among the ranks of the Crusaders but the word 'surgery' had a much wider connotation back then. It did not just include conditions that were physically visible but diseases which might at some point need an operation, too. This implied that the surgeon needed to be competent in the use of other treatments of the time such as dietary modification, drugs, blood-letting and bathing.

Arabic medical practices are rarely mentioned in contemporary Western journals and diaries compiled during and after the Crusades, but it transpires that they had a much broader and better-informed approach than their European counterparts regarding the medical needs and requirements of combatants.

In general, the Crusades were much less important to the Islamic world in the twelfth century than they were to Europe. The medieval Islamic world was so expansive that, according to most Muslim scholars, the Crusades represented little more to them than a remote frontier incident. Between the ninth and thirteenth centuries the Islamic world provided substantial contributions to the science of medicine. Caliphs and physicians established actual hospitals that provided a foundation for medical education. Physician-scientists such as al-Razi (865–925) wrote the *Kitab al-Hawi fi al-tibb* (*The Comprehensive Book on Medicine*), which provided the main medical curriculum for European schools into the fourteenth century. Mansur (1380–1422) wrote the first colour-illustrated book on anatomy. Other Islamic physicians compiled information on the use of medication from plants and advanced surgical techniques, including cataract extraction. They studied physiology, including pulmonary circulation long before their Western counterparts. These books provided the basis for medical care while Europe was still emerging from the Dark Ages.

The words hospital, hospice, hospitable and so on are derived from the Latin word '*hospitale*', which was transposed to 'Hospitaller' by the knights and their auxiliaries who adopted this suffix. The organization still exists in name to this day. During the First Crusade led, by Godfrey de Bouillon in 1096, there was no official medical provision or evidence that the armies systematically provided care for their wounded. It is likely the wounded were simply deposited at the nearest friendly town in the hope that they would receive some sort of care. After the fall of Jerusalem in 1098, various knightly orders established hospices to care for sick and wounded soldiers, as well as for pilgrims destined for the Holy Land. These are assumed by many to be the forerunners of today's modern hospitals.

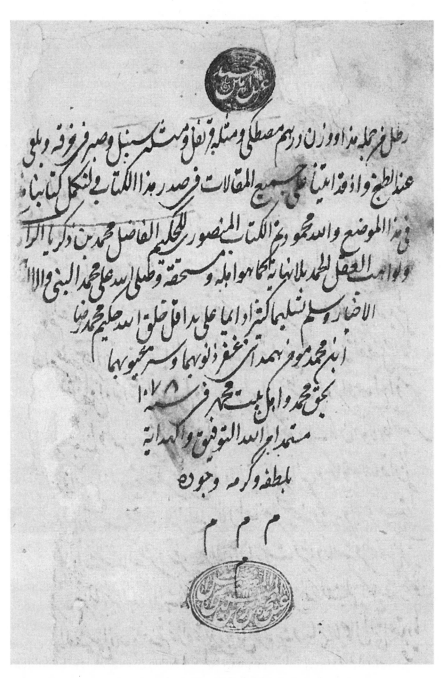

A page from al-Razi's Kitab al-Hawi fi al-tibb (The Comprehensive Book on Medicine).

It is still possible to visit what is reputedly one of the world's earliest hospitals. St John's Hospital in Bruges has an 800-year-old history of caring for pilgrims and travellers, along with the impoverished and ill citizens of that city. During the affluent Burgundian era the prosperous city of Bruges was regarded as a medieval utopia, complete with social services and quasi-medical assistance. The wards where the nuns and monks practised their dubious medical skills are still accessible to the public, as is the chapel and the impressive collection of rather intimidating-looking medical instruments and implements. The prospect alone of being on the receiving end of any of these had the potential to induce paroxysms of terror, catatonic states or even death. The latter option was preferred in most circumstances.

St John's Hospital in Bruges is reputedly the oldest hospital in the world.

There aren't many historical references to battlefield nurses before the eighteenth century, but in medieval times when men went to war they often took their families with them – and it is well documented that their womenfolk assumed the roles of erstwhile nurses for the wounded and dying during military campaigns. Removing casualties from the battlefield was another matter entirely. The first reference to any kind of stretcher occurs in a manuscript written around 1380.

Physicians were widely regarded as ostensibly skilled people, but their work was based on inadequate knowledge of human anatomy. Experiments on dead bodies were forbidden on religious grounds in medieval England. Physicians charged extortionately for their services, so only the rich could afford to pay for them. The cures they applied could be quite bizarre although some treatments, such as bleeding and the use of herbs, had real medicinal value.

One particular remedy, allegedly invented by St Paul, was a potion to treat epilepsy, catalepsy and stomach problems. Its extensive list of ingredients included liquorice, sage, willow, roses, fennel, cinnamon, ginger, cloves, cormorant blood, mandrake, dragon's blood and three kinds of pepper. Where one would acquire dragon's blood is anyone's guess, but some of the other ingredients do have proven medicinal value. Liquorice, for instance, is still used to treat coughs and bronchitis. Sage is thought to improve blood flow to the brain, and willow contains salicylic acid, a component of modern-day aspirin. Even though thunderous repetitious farting was regarded more as a means of entertainment than a passport to social exclusion, fennel, cinnamon and ginger are all acknowledged carminatives, or treatments for relieving gas in the intestines, and colic. It is, however, doubtful that the potion would have been of any use in the treatment of epilepsy and catalepsy.

Another cure was actually known as 'Dragon's blood', and was the bright red resin of the tree *Dracaena draco*, a species native to Morocco, Cape Verde and the Canary Islands. Modern research has shown that it has significant antiseptic, antibiotic, anti-viral and wound-healing properties, and it is still used today in some parts of the world to treat dysentery.

Rubbing the slime of a snail on the affected area was the medieval remedy for burns and scalds. This sounds like pure quackery, but it really did help to reduce blistering and ease pain. It's been scientifically proven that snail slime contains antioxidants,

The dark red tree resin known as Dragon's blood

31

antiseptic and anaesthetic along with anti-irritant, anti-inflammatory, antibiotic and anti-viral properties, as well as collagen and elastin, vital for skin repair. Combining barley with one handful of betony (grassland herb) and another handful of the herb vervain was a treatment for medieval headaches. Once boiled up the mixture was wrapped in a poultice that would be firmly placed on the head of the sufferer to relieve the symptoms, which it inevitably did. Betony was also used by medieval and Tudor apothecaries as an ingredient in remedies to be taken internally for all kinds of ailments.

Modern medicine still makes use of the alkaloid drugs found in betony for treating severe headaches and migraine, and vervain derivatives too are used in modern treatments for migraine, depression and anxiety. It was alleged that vervain was used to stem the flow of blood from Christ's wounds at his crucifixion. It might have proved more useful when the crown of thorns was placed on the poor man's head but that's the beauty of hindsight. In any case, it's clear that not all medieval medicine was blatant quackery.

Two medical experts from the period who were definitely not quacks were John Bradmore and Thomas Morstede. Both were dedicated surgeons employed by the Lancastrian kings Henry IV and Henry V. Bradmore played an integral and memorable part in the life of the man who would eventually become Henry V, immortalized by Shakespeare for his victory against the French at Agincourt in 1415.

A few years earlier, during the Wars of the Roses at the Battle of Shrewsbury in 1403, the-then Prince Henry, Prince of Wales, was hit square in the face by an arrow, probably fired from a crossbow, which penetrated his skull up to a depth of around 15 cm (6 in). Bradmore, who possessed only a rudimentary knowledge of cranial anatomy, mostly gained from having examined a few severed heads (which were relatively easy to procure at the time for obvious reasons), nevertheless devised an ingenious means of extracting the offending projectile.

With the wound bleeding profusely and the prince in agonizing pain – and no doubt violently accusing Bradmore of being of uncertain parentage – the medical man apparently improvised a pair of hollow tongs that were the width of an arrowhead, with a screw-like thread at the end of each arm and a separate screw mechanism running through the centre. Much to the chagrin of the prince, the wound had to be enlarged and deepened before

At the Battle of Shrewsbury in 1403 physician John Bradmore demonstrated an innovation that caused excruciating pain but saved the life of a future King.

the tongs could be inserted. This was eventually achieved by means of large and long probes made from elder stitched with linen cloth infused with rose honey.

When Bradmore determined that he had reached the bottom of the wound, he introduced the tongs at the same angle as the arrow had entered, placed the screw in the centre and manoeuvred the instrument into the socket of the arrowhead. Bradmore even had the acumen to prevent infection by treating the wound with white wine. The alcohol would have inadvertently served as a kind of disinfectant. After the wound was cleansed he packed it with wads of flax (linen) soaked in cleansing ointment, infused with an unlikely combination of bread, sops, barley, honey and turpentine oil. As the wound healed he reduced the amount of packing every two days until, 20 days after the battle, he was able to confidently report that 'The wound was perfectly well cleansed'. This was remarkably fortuitous for Bradmore, who had saved the prince and himself from a fate worse than death.

Prince Henry recovered completely and was crowned as King Henry V in 1413. Bradmore died in 1412 and was replaced by Thomas Morstede. At this juncture in history the pace quickens a little and Morstede is allowed, nay, positively encouraged, to assemble an entourage of surgeons, apprentices and medical men. Certain individuals regard this collective as one of the first professional medical corps to accompany an English fighting force. Morstede is alleged to have written extensively about his chosen métier, but his instructional work on surgery was considered lost to posterity – until an amazing recent discovery.

There is still heated debate that writings rediscovered in the last century can be attributed to Morstede or Bradmore – or neither of them. The writings detail the skills and competencies required by a battlefield surgeon along with a profound knowledge of anatomy, which, as previously stated, was widely frowned upon in the devoutly religious Middle Ages.

The Church told medieval peasants that illness was a punishment from God for sinful behaviour and, apart from the odd happy heathen, they believed this unquestioningly. Therefore, any illness was self-imposed and a direct result of the individual's sinful ways. Men like Morstede and Bradmore probably disagreed, their knowledge of pain and suffering gained by what they saw and treated on the battlefield, war and conflict being the archetypal learning grounds for many medical innovations at that time. Some of these discoveries have had a significant impact on our understanding of the body and the devastating impact of battlefield trauma on both the mind and body. The paradox was that while medical staff initiated new methods of treatment, the combatants developed deadly new ways to maim and murder, which in turn presented new challenges to the medical community.

* * *

While Western scholars were wrestling with the basics of anatomy and medicinal treatments, Chinese physicians had developed an intricate system of healing that had evolved over a few thousand years and incorporated herbal medicine, acupuncture, moxibustion, acupressure, massage and more. In the sixth century AD Japan imported the culture of Chinese medicine, mainly via the Korean peninsula, and adapted it to meet its own needs. The primary source of remedies in traditional Chinese medicine is based on the botanical and spiritual rather than the corporal. Of the more than 12,000 items used by traditional healers, around 500 are still in common use.

Chinese medicine disseminated philosophical concepts such as Yin-Yang, the Five Elements, pattern identification, and Qi and Blood that were completely alien to Western medicinal practices and considered far too abstract to be of any practical use. These concepts were often at odds with the broader anatomical knowledge being developed in Western medicine, which saw no correlation between the human body as a whole and the microcosm of the universe in diagnosis and treatment. The Chinese regarded bringing the mind, body and spirit into harmony with Yin-Yang balance as quintessential to the health and wellbeing of patients. The concept of Yin-Yang balance indicating the harmony of internal organs remains the dominating factor in traditional Chinese medicine.

The West may have rejected the employment of traditional Chinese medicine, but they had no problem using that other Chinese invention, gunpowder. Gunpowder had been used in war for a few centuries in the Far East before the West got hold of it around the fourteenth century. Its invention was reputedly established around 850 as the result of Chinese alchemists attempting to find a potion that perpetuated longevity. Gunpowder, being an extremely volatile substance, probably had the opposite effect.

Numerous armies had already used incendiary materials to deter potential assailants for hundreds of years. The most notorious concoction was known as 'Greek Fire' and many writers of antiquity refer to flaming arrows, fire pots and the use of such substances as pitch, naphtha, sulphur and charcoal. The substance could be thrown in pots or discharged, mortar-like, from tubes, whereupon it apparently caught fire spontaneously and could not be extinguished with water.

Consequently, various treatments for serious burns were also available. Hippocrates had recommended the use of bulky dressings impregnated with rendered pig fat and resin alternated with warm vinegar soaks, augmented with tanning solutions made from oak bark. In the first century AD Celsus, a Greek philosopher and ardent opponent of early Christianity, prescribed a burn lotion with bacteriostatic properties and which consisted of wine and myrrh. One of the simplest and still-used methods of treating burns was recommended around 900, by an Arabian physician of some distinction called Rhases (Muhammad ibn Zakariya al-Razi), who sensibly enough suggested dousing the afflicted area in cold water.

The true renaissance of military medicine in Europe occurred in Spain during the final decades of the fifteenth century when Spanish forces finally managed to expel Islamic Moors from their homeland. While the wars were raging, the Spanish military emulated the mobile hospitals already used by the Moorish armies. After the surrender of Malaga in 1487, the Queen's Hospital brought Spanish army casualties in 400 '*ambulancia*' (wagons) into the city to receive medical attention and a restorative visit from Queen Isabella.

It was around this time that surgeons such as Ambroise Paré began to make their appearance in French armies. As the feudal system dissipated in Europe and nations began to take shape, Europeans subsequently formed armies to defend themselves, and on occasion conquer new territory. With the new nations also came a rebirth, or renaissance, of learning. In contrast to their Western counterparts the Arab and Byzantine cultures retained many ancient Greek and Roman texts, which were then translated and reintroduced into European medicine. Unfortunately, some of the medical texts were lost in translation, which resulted in the improper treatment of certain injuries. For example, infection was often introduced into wounds in the belief that it assisted with healing, despite Greek and Roman physicians understanding that this was a wholly erroneous concept.

The introduction of gunpowder to the battlefield in the late Middle Ages meant that surgeons had to adapt their techniques accordingly. They discovered that lead balls fired from smoothbore muskets had the potential to inflict horrific wounds, particularly on limbs. Compound fractures, rare in ancient times, became commonplace due to the force of a bullet or projectile hitting a bone. Although most combatants would survive the initial injuries sustained by gunfire, other complications would inevitably develop that would ultimately prove fatal.

The primary problem for many of these injuries was that of infection. Almost all gunshot wounds became infected due to either the nature of the injury itself or filthy clothing, dirt and other contaminated material being forced into the wound when the body was impacted by the musket ball or piece of shrapnel. The situation would be further exacerbated by the dubious personal hygiene of the wounded and the unsanitary conditions they would have to endure following injury. It didn't help that the surgeon probing for the musket ball or shrapnel had unwashed, detritus-ridden fingers and hands. In the effort to promote healing there was often a high risk of death from infection rather than from the injury itself.

Personal hygiene was indeed a problem but there is sufficient evidence to suggest that in the Middle Ages most people washed at least once a week. Cleanliness was not, however, regarded as being next to godliness. While the poor would bathe in streams, rivers and lakes, the more affluent members of society would congregate in bathhouses. The Catholic Church vehemently disapproved of these notorious places and, surprisingly enough, on this occasion their vociferous objections were not entirely groundless. Many bathhouses were indeed used as brothels.

As the centuries passed personal hygiene considerations actually deteriorated, to such an extent that by the seventeenth century bathing was positively frowned upon. Consequently, people stank to high heaven and this remained the case until the advent of the Industrial Revolution in the mid-eighteenth century and the discovery of the germ theory of disease in the second half of the nineteenth century. Until then, hygiene and sanitation were not universally accepted as the reasons behind some illnesses and diseases such as cholera and typhoid.

From the late Middle Ages and for many ensuing centuries, the only acknowledged way of dealing with an afflicted limb was immediate amputation. The problem was that the surgeon's ability wouldn't be assessed on his knowledge of medicine, but on how fast he could remove the afflicted limb. Despite the advent of gunpowder and shot, the ingenuity and amazing capacity of ad hoc medical staff to adapt techniques and improvise while under fire saved countless lives in often horrific circumstances. The techniques developed in combat by surgeons such as Morstede and Bradmore would resound and disseminate throughout the world of medicine and remain with us up to the present day.

CHAPTER THREE

ARE WE THERE YET?

Ambroise Paré, who we briefly met in the last chapter, was one of the primary innovators of what we have come to regard as 'battlefield medicine' and served as a royally appointed military surgeon for a number of French kings. As well as pioneering new battlefield treatments, he radically improved on existing techniques designed for the treatment of war wounds. He began as an apprentice barber, then decided to pursue a career in medicine after witnessing French soldiers killing their wounded comrades with a *coup de grace* at the Battle of Milan in 1536. He remained in medicine for the next 30 years.

Barber-surgeons such as Paré were on occasion skilled workers who, apart from being able to provide a suitable trim and a shave, were trained by apprenticeship to perform basic surgical and other medical procedures. Young apprentices often trained under skilled barber-surgeons in the army and many remained with the army even after mastering the trade.

Movies depicting the treatment of battlefield wounds in the medieval era often show a white-hot sword or dagger being skilfully applied to cauterize and seal the affected area. The viewer is usually treated to the cringeworthy sound of searing flesh and the agonized howls of pain from the reluctant patient. For centuries, tissue exposed following an amputation would indeed be cauterized in this way. Searing the open wound often did little to stop the bleeding and the procedure itself was so terribly painful that many patients expired on the table from shock. Paré tried using ligatures to staunch post-operative bleeding. Using this technique, open arteries would be tied off using thread. The ensuing infection caused by these ligatures also had the potential to cause death, but his pioneering work has been widely acknowledged as a veritable milestone in medicine.

Another common, but equally painful method of treating open wounds was the practice of pouring boiling oil onto the afflicted area. On one occasion Paré had exhausted his personal oil supply, so he combined a tincture made from egg yolk, turpentine and oil of roses. The following morning, he was astounded to see that all the soldiers who had been treated with his tincture were in a considerably better condition than those who had been subjected to the excruciating boiling oil treatment. They also had the benefit of not smelling like cooked bacon.

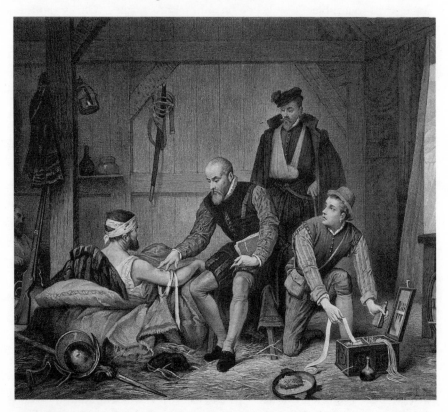

Ambroise Paré elevated the practice of treating battlefield trauma wounds to the next level.

William Harvey's observations on blood circulation, Sir Christopher Wren's intravenous administration of medicines, and Andreas Vesalius' works on human anatomy all made reference to the pioneering work of Ambroise Paré. He completely rejected cauterization for the sealing of wounds after amputation. He eventually opted exclusively for ancient Roman-style ligatures to close blood vessels because he considered this method marginally less traumatic for the patient. The absence of any kind of antiseptic still meant the ligatures could become infected, resulting in death. This deterred other surgeons from using the same technique.

Paré soldiered on and remained receptive to new ideas, such as those proposed by Flemish-born anatomist Andreas Vesalius. His 1543 book *De humani corporis fabrica* contained unprecedented contents detailing Vesalius' personal observations of human dissection. The book transformed anatomy into a subject that relied on annotations taken directly from these dissections as opposed to the perpetual guessing game employed by many barber-surgeons of the day.

Paré was also a pioneering exponent of anatomy-based treatments. Among other things, he introduced the implantation of teeth, artificial limbs, and artificial eyes made of gold and silver. He invented many scientific instruments, popularized the use of the truss for hernia, and was the first to suggest syphilis as a cause of aneurysm (the swelling of blood vessels), along with introducing revolutionary new ideas in obstetrics. He also designed an early version of a modern haemostat, which enabled the amputation of larger limbs and made it a more acceptable procedure. By 1545, Paré had collected enough knowledge of battlefield medicine to publish *The Method of Curing Wounds Caused by Arquebus and Firearms*. He was a true innovator who expertly engendered the methods of care of battlefield trauma wounds.

His famed work as a war surgeon, and afterwards as a surgeon in Paris, together with the publication of his book *Les Oeuvres* in 1575, ensured that Ambroise Paré's techniques and ideas spread across the whole of Europe. His success was also influential in initiating the rise in status of the previously feared barber-surgeons.

During the reign of Henry VIII (1509–1547) and his successors, the English Army regularly employed surgeons to care for the wounded. There were 57 surgeons present at the Battle of St Quentin in 1557 of whom 50 were designated for the rank-and-file soldiers. Most army surgeons were provided by the London Company of Barber-Surgeons, which was reputed to have employed some rather dubious practices and questionable standards. It's debatable whether or not they were familiar with the work of Paré or Vesalius.

There is no war more insidious, more heart-rending and more divisive than a civil war. During the English Civil War (1642–1651), in the aftermath of the Battle of Edgehill that occurred on 23 October 1642, scant attention was paid to the numerous casualties that resulted from this clash of arms. It is generally accepted that the Royalist Army failed to attach the same high priority to the care of its sick and wounded as its Parliamentarian counterpart did, but even so little is known of what became of the Parliamentarian wounded after that first pitched battle. The Royalist Army made no central provision for the care of sick or wounded soldiers. Most of their casualties were mercilessly left behind to rot while a lucky few were laboriously transported to Oxford in ox-drawn wagons and deposited in various churches, alms-houses, hostelries and private houses along the way with vague promises that they would be picked up later.

By this time troops were armed with a variety of weapons that included long pikes and muskets. The more fortunate soldiers had wheel-lock muskets but there were still some with matchlock firing devices, which tragically had the potential to ignite the powder pouches on the bandoliers known as the '12 Apostles' worn by musketeers. This could on occasion cause the wearer to become the unwilling subject of his own personal pyrotechnic display and be simply blown to smithereens.

Eventually, a military hospital was established in the surviving portion of the former St Mary's College. As a result of the ensuing sieges and battles, apart from the casualties incurred on the field, both Royalist and Parliamentarian armies had to contend with various epidemics resulting from poor sanitation, overcrowding, lack of food and infected water. Cholera, typhoid and even resurgence of the devastating plague afflicted thousands. Women were frequently in proximity to care for the sick and wounded but at the time were not specifically delegated as nurses.

Pious Parliamentarian commander Oliver Cromwell was rarely the life and soul of any party. He was a notoriously miserable person who would eventually have the temerity to cancel Christmas. But he got some priorities right. When he introduced his New Model Army in 1645 he appointed a physician general, a surgeon general and an apothecary general. It followed the standard of requiring one surgeon for each company, which the designated guilds were obliged to supply if there were not enough volunteers. Parliament provided medicines that were for internal use, but the surgeons were still required to provide external medicines, such as liniments and ointments and the dressings for the wounds, the cost of which was ultimately funded by the troops. Given the number of casualties, the resources of the regimental hospitals soon became overburdened with sick and wounded soldiers. At the start of the conflict, many of the wounded were given financial assistance and sent home.

Sustaining a wound in the English Civil War was a particularly agonizing experience. Soldiers were treated with bullet extractors, bone saws and skull

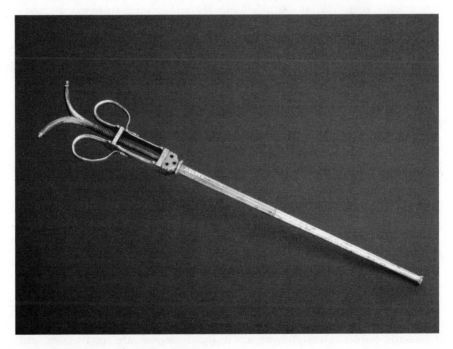

A sixteenth-century musket ball extractor.

elevators. Anaesthetic hadn't yet been developed, and some of the cures actually worsened the predicament of sufferers. There was no shortage of wounded personnel to practise on. Musket balls, cannons, typhus and dysentery took their toll, but it's surprising how many survived frequently horrific injuries.

The seventeenth century saw the advent of attempts to perform cranial surgery. Evidently a seventeenth-century neurosurgeon kept his fingernails long in preparation for the removal of an exposed pericranium. Most physicians back in the day possessed a reasonable knowledge of anatomy but dismal ignorance of actual brain function. Some astrologer-surgeons believed that it was dangerous to use a trephine (a hole saw used in surgery to remove a circle of tissue or bone) during a full moon because they thought that on such occasions the brain was enlarged and too close to the patient's skull.

There is evidence to propose that some practitioners were aware of the phenomenon of a post-traumatic cerebral oedema, even if not of its underlying mechanism. One surgeon recommending trephination for a comminuted fracture of the skull stated, 'This should be undertaken when the patient had recovered from the immediate shock but not after the third day, the operation would then be fraught with danger.' But it would always draw a good crowd and provide a bloodthirsty spectacle for the spectators, who had seriously distorted views on precisely what constituted entertainment. Such spectacles could have contravened the Parliamentary decree that forbade, among other things, 'Spectacles of pleasure, too commonly expressing lascivious mirth and levity'. It is, however, safe to assume that the recipient of the surgeons' and spectators' attentions rarely expressed either lascivious mirth or levity.

In response to a conflict which reduced England's population by about six per cent, Parliament established the first permanent military hospitals. In 1642 a viable welfare system was initiated for troops and their families that provided actual nurses. There were many war widows among this collective who were designated with changing linen and towels weekly, deep-cleaning hospitals and prescribing trips to the restorative waters of Bath.

As the civil war progressed, casualties mounted and recruits became more difficult to procure and concrete arrangements were made for the care of the sick and wounded. In London, a central facility was established at the Savoy Hospital in 1644, with Parliament paying its physicians and surgeons through its Committee for Sick and Maimed Soldiers. This and other such organizations were the result of the terrible casualties incurred by both sides. Estimates of war-related deaths during this time were almost 18 times greater than those suffered by the British in World War II. The number of wounded was estimated at over 90,000 for England and Wales; 30,000 for Scotland; and between 80,000 and 100,000 for Ireland.

In the early 1700s, during the reign of Queen Anne, one of her favourites, John Churchill, the Duke of Marlborough, prepared his army for war. As de facto leader of allied forces in the Low Countries, he secured spectacular victories at Blenheim (1704), Ramillies (1706), Oudenarde (1708) and Malplaquet (1709), which enshrined his place in history as one of Europe's great generals. There is reference to the presence of nurses in various contemporary documents along with the venerable quality of the care provided in Marlborough's army hospitals, which is also frequently attested to.

In 1701 John Hudson, who had been responsible for the administration of the army's hospital in Bruges, was asked to propose an establishment for a hospital to exclusively provide for the army. Hudson responded with a list of minimum requirements, based on the optimistic assumption that 'there will be not less than a thousand sick in an army of 18,000 men'. No less than three physicians, three master surgeons, three surgeon's mates, one master apothecary and four apothecary's mates would be provided. Hudson's proposals were accepted and he was officially appointed Controller of His Majesty's Town and Field Hospital in Flanders.

Hudson also specified that stores of medicines and utensils for the sick and wounded should be assembled in addition to the surgeons' chests and instruments issued to each battalion. All these supplies would have to be viewed and approved by the physician general and the surgeon general prior to dispatch. Campaigning in the early eighteenth century was seasonal and Hudson's estimates were based on the concept of a standard non-negotiable 200-day campaign season, which would ensure all incumbents being home for Christmas.

One of the many reasons Marlborough was a successful commander was due to his appointment of an Apothecary General who provided each regiment with a chest of medicines.

In addition to providing a static hospital, Hudson's responsibilities extended to providing mobile or 'flying' field hospitals. Once the Captain General had informed him of the location where a hospital was to be sited, decisions would be made regarding the reception of sick and wounded soldiers into either British or Dutch hospitals. They would then be provided with food, accommodation, drugs and the attention of physicians and surgeons.

There was a fiscally motivated reason to avoid getting wounded because soldiers were expected to pay for these facilities. There was, however, a modicum of altruism that ensured anyone admitted to an army hospital facility would receive financial assistance to pay for the care provided. A barometer of nutritional intake was also observed and regulations were introduced to accommodate those suffering from relatively minor sicknesses or injuries. In addition to their normal daily pay in local currency each patient would receive an extra daily allowance to cover additional costs. Patients that were very ill or seriously injured, and presumably consumed less food, would receive a marginally lesser allowance. The unofficial advice was, 'don't get wounded, it'll cost you, but the food in Flanders is rather good'.

Hudson made a commitment to report personally to Marlborough every week or fortnight, depending on the circumstances, to brief him on the state of the hospitals. The Apothecary General agreed to furnish each regiment with a chest of medicines, but made a distinction between officers and men when he added that there should 'be particular provision of medicines to attend in the field for the use of the General or other officers'. This didn't particularly endear him to the rank and file.

Efforts aimed at promoting good health and sanitation guaranteed that every responsible officer on land or at sea was required to ensure that their soldiers' quarters were kept clean and tidy 'upon pain of severe punishment'. Statutory articles imposed an attempt to limit cross-infection by requiring the immediate removal of anyone who became sick or had been wounded. They were taken from their regimental lines into accommodation where they could be treated and hopefully recover under the supervision of a responsible officer.

The sick and wounded soldiers were allowed to draw pay until a qualified surgeon or physician determined that they were unable to resume military service. Strict rules were applied when a soldier died on active duty. His former captain was tasked with providing funds to the next-of-kin or legally entitled beneficiaries. Anyone who misappropriated a dead soldier's belongings would be compelled to refund double their assessed value to the rightful heirs.

Hudson was one of the first appointed civil servants to acknowledge the presence of nursing staff in his annual accounts. He meticulously detailed payments made to the junior hospital staff, listed as 'servants', including 'nurses' that attended the sick and wounded men, along with a butler and a cook together and their assistants, a washer-woman and a porter who ran errands and drew water from the well.

Hudson's annual purchases of food for the army amounted to 5,809 pounds of mutton, beef and veal, 6,076 loaves of bread, 6,360 cans of beer (in this context the contemporary use of 'can' referred to a cup measure of varying capacity), 825 pounds of cheese, 478 pounds of rice, 1,712 bushels of oatmeal, 280 pounds of sugar, 382 quarts of wine and brandy, 2,050 eggs and 92 pounds of butter. Milk was acquired in large quantities and used in a variety of dietary preparations, including 'posset drinks' for the weaker patients. This libation was originally a popular British hot drink made of milk curdled with wine or ale, often spiced, which during a campaign was often used as a remedy for those who were ailing or recovering from wounds. Salt, herbs and spices added flavour to broth, gruel and milk drinks as well as mulled wine or brandy. Hudson strongly believed in sourcing items from local communities such as turf and charcoal used for both heating and cooking, candles, wood, soap for washing the men's linen, as well as fresh straw to renew the hospital bed mattresses.

Marlborough's army endured two years of relatively static warfare in the Low Countries, but in 1704 this well-tuned war machine went into action. For ten years Marlborough was victorious time after time against a military superpower that had remained undefeated for over 60 years. In a long and relatively eclectic military career that ended with the Jacobite rising in 1715, he fought with the French against the Dutch, the Dutch against the French, with the Catholic James against the Protestant Monmouth and the Protestant William against the Catholic James. Here was the commander who could knock the polish off the Sun King and demonstrate the right way to win a campaign in the process.

Marlborough proved his military genius on numerous occasions. Moreover, he managed to maintain cohesion in a fragile alliance and lay the foundations of modern warfare. His army was feared throughout Europe and terrified enemies in a European war that stretched from Spain to the Danube, and from Italy to the Low Countries. Marlborough tried, tested and proved the intrinsic value of efficient medical services and the importance of a well-protected supply train to a campaigning army. A healthy army was an effective one and a dreadful prospect for its adversaries.

It was the glorious age of enlightenment and it had taken decennia for military commanders to finally get a grasp on the rudimentary requirements of an army on the march. Naturally there were still the rape, looting and pillaging to contend with but these were usually of a temporary nature.

Medical innovations were on the increase and although there was still a long way to go before the advent of bactericides, at least efforts were being undertaken to recognize and deal with the physical maladies that beset soldiers in combat.

In 1718 the French surgeon Jean Louis Petit invented a screw tourniquet to control bleeding. It made thigh amputations possible and reduced the risks associated with amputations below the knee. The screw tourniquet was still widely in use during the American Civil War. As amputations became safer, military surgeons gave greater emphasis to preparing limbs for prosthesis. Flap and lateral incision amputations became common procedures. Nevertheless, the death rate from amputation remained high until methods were developed in the nineteenth century to control infection and shock.

Before women were allowed officially to serve as nurses, their role as caregivers was horribly stereotyped: as 'loving wives' when caring for a sick husband, or asexual nuns, serving God and his ailing legions, or worse still as the much-maligned 'camp followers', women of ill repute who would do anything for an army on the march for money – including nursing the sick. Women were most definitely not accepted as 'proper' health workers until at least the middle of the eighteenth century, apart, that is, from the amazing Sisters of the Beguine.

This wonderful collective didn't provide any nursing care on the battlefield but they would most certainly have tended Crusader knights and their entourages that made it back to their communes (Beguinages) from the Holy Land. In 1302 the Sisters found themselves directly in the firing line after the 'Battle of the Golden Spurs'. The scenario for this battle is remarkably similar to the one fought by Henry V and his host some years later at Agincourt. This particular battle occurred on the Groeningheveld just outside the Flemish market town of Kortrijk. The French/Burgundian army consisted mainly of heavily armoured cavalry. Contrary to popular Flemish folklore, the adversaries were primarily town militia who were well equipped and well trained. They were organized by guild affiliation,

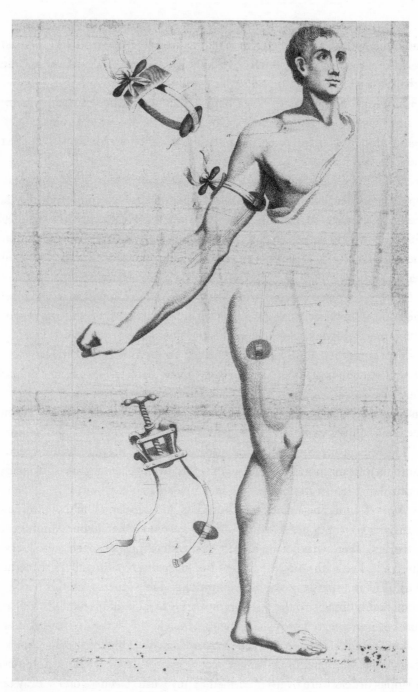

A diagram of Petit's screw tourniquet.

and equipped with steel helmets, chainmail haubergeons, pikes, bows and crossbows and numbered around 9,000, including 400 noblemen. The urban Flemish militias of the time prided themselves on their regular training and preparation. The Flemish militia formed a line formation against cavalry with pikes pointed outward. Because of the high rate of defections among the Flemish nobility, there were few mounted knights on the Flemish side.

The eventual result looked seemingly inevitable but the Flemish had chosen their battlefield. Most of the area was inundated and boggy, which wasn't conducive to the cumbersome attire of the French/Burgundian knights, who consequently got stuck in the mud. Flemish peasants seized the opportunity to maraud and dispatch these knights. The battle soon became a rout.

Among the victors' trophies were numerous golden spurs purloined from the boots of the French knights, which provided the title for this encounter. When retreating French/Burgundian knights discovered wounded Flemish soldiers being treated at a local Beguinage, the place was levelled and many of the wounded including some sisters were brutally murdered. Despite this setback the Sisters of the Beguine survived wars, crusades, plagues and famines and continued to provide deeply appreciated and respected care in the communities in which they lived.

The reason the Sisters existed in the first place was due to the rise of those mendicant monastic orders in the late twelfth century and thirteenth century that led to an unusual gender imbalance in northern Europe. The feudal system defined strict rules for class and gender, which left women with very few options. A woman could live under her father's roof until betrothed, then with her husband until widowed. Then, if she was lucky, she could live with one or more of her offspring. Failing all of that, she could live as a spinster, which could mean enduring accusations of being a witch and risking the ducking stool or worse. Finally, she could don a habit, take vows and become a respectable nun.

The problem was that there were so many unmarried, widowed or abandoned women in northern Europe, especially in Belgium, that the religious orders were over-subscribed. They were turning women away or fleecing their families for bigger contributions before accepting them. The

The Sisters of the Beguines were a formidable collective that ran the hospitals and provided care in the many communities where they lived and thrived in the Middle Ages.

Cistercians actually closed their order to women for a time. But necessity being the mother of invention meant that one group of women in Belgium, with no intention of becoming anyone's mother or sister, got together and created a new space for themselves in society. It was an organization for unmarried women who were willing to work hard and live pious lives.

The Sisters of the Beguine was in effect a kind of women's liberation movement. Its members led a communal lifestyle, dedicating themselves to God, prayer, nursing and social care – but they stringently avoided taking vows or having any connection to the Catholic Church's all-powerful and domineering hierarchy. The name 'beguine' may have come from the beige colour of their habits, but there are other theories on how the name originated. It may have been borrowed from Medieval French, being a feminine derivative of *begard*, meaning the male member of a lay order. The biggest difference between beguines and nuns was that beguines could leave the community to get married without any repercussions. If a nun attempted to leave her order she risked excommunication or, in some cases, death.

The Beguines became respected and valued members of Bruges and Burgundian society for many years. They thrived until 1311, when the Council of Vienne issued the decree *Ad nostrum*, which accused the Beguines of being antinomian 'heretics of the Free Spirit' and set in motion decades of persecution that almost eradicated the order. Survivors had their property confiscated and were forced to marry. Then the organization was saved, when Pope John XXII issued the papal bull *Racio recta*, which stated that the Beguines should be permitted to 'pursue their way of life without diminution of property or rights'. Rome was becoming increasingly paranoid at the prospect of new religious orders being formed. In 1421 Pope Martin V ordered the archbishop of Cologne to 'search out and destroy any small convents of persons living under the cloak of religion without a definite Rule'. The Beguines shouldn't really have been a matter of consternation for Pope Martin because beguinages were essentially poorhouses and hospitals, which were not preoccupied with theological concerns. The Sisters of the Beguine remained active until the Reformation dissolved them, although the beguinages in Belgium had something of a revival in the seventeenth century. In 1969, there were still 11 beguinages in Belgium and two in Holland. Despite centuries of adversity they survived and their members continued to provide essential care in the community. They were nurses.

During the English Civil War a woman named Lucy Apsley, the daughter of Sir Allen Apsley, the Lieutenant of the Tower of London, provided 'nursing care' for the wounded. At the age of 18 she was married in Nottingham to John Hutchinson, a wealthy landowner. Both Lucy Hutchinson and her husband were devout Baptists at a time when religion took precedence over military acumen and everything that occurred was ascribed to the will of God. During the civil war John became an officer in the Parliamentary Army and Lucy worked as a nurse. After the war, she recounted her experiences and mentioned that after one particular battle she extended her nursing ability to care for wounded men of the opposing Royalist Army. 'In the encounter only five of our men were hurt, we dressed all their wounds with such success that they were all cured. Seeing three of the prisoners badly bleeding I dressed their wounds also. Captain Palmer came in and told me not to help the enemies of God. I replied, I had a duty to treat them as men, not as enemies.'

After the Restoration John Hutchinson was arrested on the grounds that he had been one of the signatories of Charles I's death warrant. He died in prison in 1664. In 1670, Lucy Hutchinson finished *Memoirs of the Life of Colonel Hutchinson* but it was considered too inflammatory and anti-monarchist to be published. More importantly, by her wartime deeds she had established the wonderfully unambiguous contribution that frontline medical staff could make when caring for the wounded of both sides. Lucy Hutchinson died sometime around 1680.

It's possible that the events of the English Civil War inspired a certain Mrs Elizabeth Alkin to write this letter to a Parliamentary naval committee in July 1655:

'Mr. Blackbourne,
'I implore you presenting humble service to all my Masters, and to your self, Sir you have sent me down to Harwich with five pounds, but believe me it has cost me three times as much, since my coming

hither, I have laid out my moneys for diverse necessaries about
the sick & wounded men here, it pities me, to see poor people in
distress, I cannot see them want if I have it, a great deal of moneys I
have given to have them cleansed, in their bodies and their hair cut
mending their clothes, reparations and several things else.'

In that same century there were other indications of women taking on
altruistic roles as nurses tending the war wounded. The Thirty Years'
War, though pre-eminently a German struggle between 1618 and 1648,
was one of the worst crises in European military history. It was a series of
catastrophic conflicts inside the Holy Roman Empire and caused the virtual
breakdown of many domestic economies, as well as famines and pandemics.
It is well documented during this war that women worked as cooks, nurses,
tailors, washerwomen and barmaids, and were considered an integral and
indispensable part of the war economy. These camp followers even received
pillaged goods and on occasion personally indulged in heinous plunder.

Many soldiers still took their women and children to war with
them, which meant that part of an army's baggage train was simply an
accumulation of itinerant households. The women in the train were subject
to military justice, and they were required to help fortify camps. Soldiers
and officers who attempted to exempt their female dependents caused great
consternation among their fellow officers and troops. As a rule, the women
and the whole train of non-combatants were under the surveillance of an
officer who was disparagingly referred to as the *hurenwaibel* (overseer of
whores).

It was partly thanks to such derogatory references that, during the late
seventeenth century, nursing as a reputable métier dissipated. In Britain
during the Reformation most monasteries were shut down along with the
hospitals they housed. The nuns that had been working as nurses were forced
to leave the profession and stay at home. This caused a general stagnation in
the profession between the seventeenth and eighteenth centuries in Europe,
except in areas where Catholicism held sway, but even there the role of
nurses decreased quite dramatically along with their numbers.

This inspired those who wished to remain practising to diversify and
develop new services such as offering care as erstwhile community nurses

to those within the estate of their patrons. While these nurses resided at the estate they would be required to perform tasks typically undertaken by apothecaries, physicians and surgeons. While nursing faced more tumultuous times during the years to come, the demand for nurses actually increased along with the almost reverential preference by the public to be treated by a caring nurse as opposed to a dangerous doctor. The medical profession still had a long way to go but there were certain individuals who began to recognize the importance of nurses, particularly on the battlefield.

During the American War of Independence (1775–1783), the Continental Congress authorized one surgeon to serve in each regiment. Few of the regimental surgeons had any experience treating trauma. They were mostly trained through the apprenticeship system because at that time there were only two medical schools in the colony (King's College, now Columbia University, in New York, NY, and the University of Pennsylvania in Philadelphia, PA). The organization was minimal, and regimental surgeons tended to work for their unit instead of seeing themselves as part of the Hospital Department, which was rendered ineffective by bureaucratic infighting. The medical officers assigned to each Continental Army regiment had more often than not served their apprenticeships with a qualified physician or surgeon, rather than having experienced a formal education. They were paid poorly and it was alleged that they often dipped into the funds they were given to purchase medicine and supplies to supplement their low pay. At the start of the war, there were 3,500 physicians and surgeons living in America, but only 400 of them had medical degrees. In 1756, the post of Inspector of Regimental Infirmaries was established to ensure that professional standards were maintained, that money collected was properly accounted for, and that patients received proper care.

In July 1775, Congress chose George Washington to command the Continental Army besieging Boston. That same month, Congress also established the Army Medical Department and appointed Dr Benjamin Church as its first Director General and Chief Physician of the Hospital of the Army. In the eighteenth century, women were a visible part of any army encampment. Some of these women were the wives of soldiers who simply

Dr Benjamin Church, first Director General of the Army Medical Department.

trailed along, having nowhere else to go. Other women offered their services for pay, as cooks, washerwomen, nurses, prostitutes or seamstresses.

The introduction of female nurses to formally accompany the Continental Army was due to Washington responding to a plea by General Horatio Gates that 'the sick suffer much for want of good female nurses'. The army preferred female nurses to male ones. In response to this request Congress authorized one nurse for every ten patients and one matron for every ten nurses. Congress allowed a salary of $2 per month for these nurses; matrons were paid $4 per month. To provide a means of caring for sick soldiers, Congress also authorized the formation of hospitals. Despite Congressional efforts to increase the number of female nurses for the army, there remained a shortage throughout the war as regiments constantly sought women to nurse their sick and wounded. The generals and officers of these regiments used all possible means to coerce women into working as nurses and even threatened to withhold rations from those who refused to volunteer.

Serving as a nurse in the Continental Army was a precarious choice of vocation. Although they received regular pay and job security was good, nursing in the army was potentially life-threatening. Exposure to deadly diseases such as smallpox and camp fevers could cause early death, and it still wasn't generally regarded as a respectable profession for ladies. Throughout the revolutionary wars disease rather than battle injuries was the main cause of death among the ranks.

Precisely how valuable nursing staff were to Washington's army is borne out by the story of Philadelphia housewife and nurse Lydia Darragh, who according to legend on the night of 2 December 1777 single-handedly saved the lives of General George Washington and his Continental Army when she overheard the British planning a surprise attack scheduled for the following day. Whether this actually happened has never been definitely ascertained, but at that time it helped to elevate the status of nurses among the troops.

The courageous women who offered their services to the army were embarking on a journey that offered discomposure, hardship and was fraught with danger. In addition to supporting the army and its irrefutable cause, they toiled hard to make a living for themselves and their families.

The contributions of Revolutionary War-era women may have long since been assigned to posterity, but it's equally important to recount their bravery and sacrifice in the same breath as the fighting men they supported. In the words of Abigail Adams in a letter to her husband John Adams on 31 March 1776: 'I desire you would remember the ladies.'

CHAPTER FOUR

HATS OFF TO LARREY!

One of the true pioneers of battlefield surgery and a primary exponent of the humanitarian approach to it was Dr Dominique-Jean Larrey (1766–1842), who also played an integral part in recognizing and endorsing the value of well-trained nurses on the battlefield. He has been described as the true father of modern military surgery, and is considered even by today's standards as the model military surgeon.

Triage is a French word that refers to the process of determining the priority of patients' treatments based on the severity of their condition, time and the treatment possibilities. The word may have originated from Larrey's work in order to determine the order and priority of emergency treatment. He also introduced the use of mobile medical units, which he named *ambulances volantes* ('flying ambulances'), that were inspired by the Napoleonic two-wheeled gun carriages and applied the method of speedy evacuation of wounded soldiers from the battlefield during combat. Larrey spent almost 18 years with Napoleon, accompanying him in 25 campaigns, 60 battles and more than 400 engagements.

He was born on 8 July 1766 in Beaudéan, in the picturesque Campan Valley. When his father, the village cobbler, died in 1770 when Larrey was just 14, the teenager decided not to dedicate himself to the family business but to a career in medicine. His uncle Alexis Larrey was the chief surgeon of the Grave Hospital at Toulouse and probably inspired this decision. Uncle Alex welcomed the lad with open arms and enrolled him at Esquille College, which was run by the Brothers of the Christian Doctrine. At the end of 1787, Larrey applied for and secured a position as a surgeon in the French Royal Navy. On his way to accept his appointment at the port of Brest he stopped by the house of Ambroise Paré.

In 1797 Larrey was appointed surgeon-in-chief of the Napoleonic armies in Italy and later saw action during the French campaign in Egypt at the first Battle of Aboukir on 25 July 1799. Respect and admiration for the doctor grew tremendously because of his battlefield activities. He didn't stay at the rear of the army and wait for casualties; he flung himself into the fray, ducking musket balls and shrapnel to treat men where they fell – French soldiers and Mamelukes alike. One grateful Mameluke even gave Larrey a talisman ring that he treasured and wore at the Battle of Waterloo.

After the battle of Aboukir, Larrey's superiors criticized his impetuous behaviour, but the wounded expressed genuine gratitude for the doctor's courage. When the French troops were being evacuated, Larrey insisted that the wounded soldiers be repatriated first and personally organized their transportation to Toulon. Soon after, Larrey developed an interest in treating the causes of scurvy, dysentery and other conditions that blighted Napoleon's troops in Egypt. He also highlighted the importance of hygiene to the troops. Personal hygiene had never been a great priority for Napoleon. Quite the opposite, in fact, and he once famously sent Josephine the written instruction: 'Don't wash my love, I will be home soon'.

The war in Egypt revealed the surgeon's ability to supervise the care and treatment of those wounded in action, a fact that didn't go unrecognized by Napoleon Bonaparte. When Dr Larrey returned to Paris he was appointed chief surgeon of the Consular Guard. At the beginning of the nineteenth century Napoleon had stated his unambiguous views on military medicine, but his actions didn't always reflect his opinions. In 1800, he had a less than favourable idea about the French army medical service: 'There is no medical service in the proper sense of the term.' Yet he apparently had high regard for Dominique-Jean Larrey.

The epitome of courage, ingenuity and innovation, Dominique-Jean Larrey was Napoleon's personal favourite.

Larrey's pioneering thesis on amputations in 1803 earned him wide recognition in the medical world and one year later, at the age of 38, he was officially appointed the 'First Doctor' and received the esteemed *Legion d'honneur*, France's highest commendation, which was personally bestowed by Napoleon Bonaparte who told him, 'Your work is one of the greatest conceptions of our age, it alone will suffice to ensure your reputation.'

During the disastrous 1812 Russian campaign Larrey was chief surgeon of the Grande Armée. The consummate organizer, in preparation he assembled all his surgeons in Berlin and gave them specific instructions to divide their staff into six 'ambulance divisions'. At the pivotal battles of Smolensk, Borodino and the retreat from Moscow he performed no less than 200 amputations. The retreat became a real test of courage and tenacity for the Grande Armée. Lacking any serious logistical support and forced to endure withering Russian winter conditions, the retreat soon deteriorated into a rout.

Starved and exhausted, thousands of Napoleon's men succumbed to the elements while others experienced a serious breakdown of humanity and lost all semblance of civilization. One French sergeant wrote of an instance where an ambulance driver fell asleep, leaving the horse that pulled his ambulance unattended. During the night soldiers killed and ate the horse, rendering the ambulance surplus to requirements. Much to Larrey's chagrin most ambulances had already exceeded their usefulness by this stage of the retreat. As the number of wounded and diseased men increased, there was little that could be done for them without access to the necessary supplies. Preferring not to remain in proximity to the sick and risk contracting their illnesses, ambulance drivers frequently ejected and abandoned their ailing cargo beside the road.

The soldiers who managed to reach the Berezina River and escape the marauding Cossacks were in a desultory state. The French crossed the Berezina between 26 and 29 November, and despite the incredibly brave exploits of the pontoon makers whole battalions disappeared beneath the ice, never to surface again. Larrey wrote how he almost perished at the crossing. He made it over the bridge on two consecutive occasions to save his equipment and surgical instruments. During the third attempt to navigate the crowd of soldiers one of them mentioned his name. Such

An example of Larrey's horse-drawn 'flying ambulances' from the French First Republic.

was the respect and reverence for the doctor that he was carried above the troops like a rock star doing a stage dive into an adoring audience until he reached the end of the bridge and safety.

Despite having to deal with the horrendous conditions Larrey and some of his staff continued to perform their duties. Exhausted and suffering from typhoid, he arrived in Königsberg on 21 December 1812. The hospitals there admitted about 10,000 of Napoleon's soldiers, but the overworked hospital staff realized that most of them were not wounded but were suffering from weather-related conditions such as frozen extremities. Physicians of that time referred to frostbite as a pest, a fever of congelation, which was terribly contagious. When the heroic Larrey arrived at the hospitals he quickly succumbed to this illness. Doctor Jacobi, and old friend, gradually helped to restore his health.

The precise number of casualties from the 1812 campaign will probably never be known. It's estimated that Napoleon's Grand Armée began the invasion with around 650,000 men of which only 93,000 survived. Roughly 370,000 died of wounds, illness or exposure to the elements while the

Russians captured around 200,000. Many of these prisoners also perished, while others are reputed to have settled in Russia.

Such was his all-pervading influence on the French, Napoleon was able to raise 300,000 men within three months of his return to Paris. In the ensuing battles, Larrey again displayed exceptional bravery on repeated occasions and was personally responsible for the evacuation of wounded French soldiers under attack by the dreaded Cossacks at the Heurtebise farm at the 1814 Battle of Craonne. Larrey remained fiercely loyal to his emperor and flatly refused to offer preferential treatment to the officers. He wrote: 'General de Sparre was brought to my ambulance wounded. He demanded immediate attention, but, after examining his wound, I thought there were far more urgent cases to attend, so despite his protests, I made him wait his turn. I did the same with the Marshal Victor, Generals Grouchy and Cambronne, even though I regarded these men as my dear friends.'

When Napoleon was forced to abdicate, Larrey requested to accompany the emperor into exile on the island of Elba. This request was refused because Napoleon wanted Larrey to remain with the soldiers of his beloved 'Old Guard'. Napoleon reciprocated Larrey's devotion by saying that 'If the army ever erects a monument to express its gratitude, it should do so in honour of Larrey.'

At Napoleon's final battle at Waterloo, Larrey received two sword cuts and was stabbed by a Prussian lance. Bleeding badly, he was captured and stripped almost naked by the Prussians, then brought before a general who demanded the doctor's immediate execution. The commander of the Prussian army, 74-year-old Marshal Blücher, intervened on Larrey's behalf and spared his life on the premise that the doctor had saved the life of his son by caring for him on a battlefield a few years earlier. Larrey finally arrived back in Paris on 15 September 1815.

Afterwards, when many of Napoleon's men were tried as Bonapartists, the doctor remarkably retained his titles and function. Larrey avoided imprisonment during the restoration of the French monarchy due to a highly complimentary report of his war services submitted by soldiers of all nationalities. On 8 April 1818, after 28 years of service, he ended his glorious career in the military at the age of 49.

Many historians claim that Larrey was an extremely egotistic, narcissistic man who frequently projected his vanity with malice. It is indisputable, however, that Larrey's conduct during the Napoleonic Wars may have inspired the creation of the Red Cross and even the establishment of the Geneva Convention. His name is engraved on the Arc de Triomphe in Paris, but it was ultimately his humane approach to caring for the wounded regardless of allegiances or nationalities that remains a guide to doctors whenever they are compelled to decide between duty to their patients and pressure from the authorities.

Over on the English side during the Napoleonic Wars, it's irrefutable that some of Admiral Lord Nelson's surgeons were rough 'sawbones' whose only skill was their ability to hack off limbs and pull teeth. Sir William Dillon said of his surgeon, Thomas Grey, 'Although an excellent scholar, being near-sighted with a defect in one of his eyes, we did not place much reliance on his ability at amputation.' The prospect of having a limb removed by a half-blind surgeon would not have inspired a lot of confidence from the patient. Thankfully, this deficiency didn't apply to all naval surgeons and at

A naval surgeon's equipment, 1793.

least some of them were well educated and qualified in their field. Despite this, the average death rate from amputation was around 33 per cent.

To become a naval surgeon in the eighteenth and early nineteenth century, the candidate had to serve a lengthy apprenticeship with a practising surgeon ashore. Time could then be spent in a university or local hospital to learn the basics of anatomy, physiology and pharmacology. Once they had acquired sufficient knowledge, they proceeded to the College of Surgeons in London for a rigorous examination. The Court of Examiners of the College of Surgeons would inform the navy at what level the newly qualified surgeon could serve on His Majesty's ships. Only the best were considered competent enough to become fully fledged ship's surgeons. Most became a surgeon's mate, and were denoted by their aptitude as first, second or third class.

The college would specify the size of ship on which the appointed surgeon could serve, and the kind of medical instruments they would need. With the onset of the Napoleonic Wars Royal Navy surgeons were obliged to buy their own instruments and chest. A representative of the College of Surgeons would meticulously check these before allowing the surgeon to join the ship.

The surgeon's work quarters were usually located on the Orlop deck, below the waterline. Despite being claustrophobic, dark and oppressive this was regarded as a comparatively safe area during a sea battle. The pungent, rancid air emanating from the bilges wouldn't have helped much either. Due to the low ceiling the surgeon would have constantly had to stoop. In the heat of battle as 32-pounder guns boomed away above the surgeon's head it was not necessarily the most placid working environment. Imagine attempting to remove a limb as the ship releases a thunderous broadside or, even worse, receives one full on. When the ship wasn't actively engaged in combat, the sickbay would be situated in a partitioned area on a higher deck with better light and air quality.

One of the most compelling accounts of naval warfare during the Napoleonic era can be found in the log written by Robert Young, who served on board HMS *Ardent*. It's difficult to envisage the absolute cacophony and chaos that would have ensued when these timber-framed leviathans received a broadside from all guns. Metal against wood was always a mismatch and while the surgeon, up to his ankles in warm blood, attempted to focus and perform his tasks, cannonballs would have been impacting in dangerously close proximity. Young relates the appalling conditions he endured during the Battle of Camperdown on 11 October 1797: 'I was employed in operating and dressing till near four in the morning, the action beginning about one in the afternoon. So great was my fatigue that I began several amputations, under a dread of sinking before I should have secured the blood vessels. Ninety wounded were brought down during the action, the whole cockpit deck, cabins wing berths, and part of the cable tier, together with my platform, and my preparation for dressing were covered with them. So that for a time, they were laid on each other at the foot of the ladder.'

A particularly debilitating illness that surgeons had to deal with during more sedentary times was venereal disease. The remedies they used were a potential passion killer to all but the most determined matelots. The condition was usually treated by applying mercury to the afflicted parts and hoping for the best. Astringent injections of white vitriol (zinc sulphate) or barley water under the prepuce or down the urethra were also frequently prescribed. If your legs haven't crossed already, one surgeon suggested half an ounce of a concoction of Epsom salts and sugar of lead, 'to be injected down the yard [penis]'. This would be followed by one dram of gum Arabic dissolved in three ounces of water if the scalding persisted, which it inevitably would. These treatments may not have cured the sailors' maladies but they would have definitely dampened their ardour for a while, if not permanently.

The year 1797 was a busy one for Britain's naval forces. In July 1797 Nelson was hit in the right arm by a musket ball shortly after stepping ashore to lead a doomed assault on the Spanish island of Tenerife. Bleeding profusely, he was taken back to HMS *Theseus* where the injured limb was quickly amputated. On 25 July the ship's surgeon, James Farquhar, wrote in his journal, 'Compound fracture of the right arm by a musket ball passing thro a little above the elbow; an artery divided; the arm was immediately amputated'. It is claimed that within 30 minutes of what must have been an unimaginably agonizing procedure Nelson was up and about and yelling orders to his men. On 1 August Farquhar noted: 'Admiral Nelson;

amputated arm; continued getting well very fast. Stump looked well; no bad symptoms whatever occurred.'

A year later, while commanding HMS *Vanguard* at the Battle of the Nile, Nelson received a musket ball in his head fired by a French navy sniper, but still managed to secure a resounding victory. The surgeon's log describes the treatment administered: 'Wound on the forehead over the right eye, the cranium is bare for more than an inch, the wound three inches long. Discharged 1 September. The wound was perfectly healed on the first September but as the integuments were much enlarged, I applied (every night) a compress wet with a discutient embrocation for nearly a month which was of great service.'

In 1805 the surgeon Sir William Beatty tended Admiral Lord Horatio Nelson during his dying moments at the Battle of Trafalgar. The surgeon distinguished himself as 96 of 102 casualties incurred during the action, including nine of the 11 amputees, survived to tell the tale. However, the nature and cause of Nelson's mortal wounds were intentionally omitted

Nelson's limb was amputated at the Battle of the Nile but according to legend (and personal accounts) he was issuing orders again half an hour later.

from the naval journal of HMS *Victory*. Experts at the National Archives in Kew believe the omission was entirely deliberate, because the budding and ambitious author Beatty wanted to save the details for publication in his own book, *Authentic Narrative of the Death of Lord Nelson*, published in 1807.

In his account, Beatty suggested that a division of a large branch of the left pulmonary artery was the cause of Lord Nelson's death. But what was the precise nature of Nelson's fatal wound? The French musket ball that did the damage struck Nelson on the left shoulder at the epaulette, with a force that threw him onto his knees. It smashed two ribs and tore through his left lung severing a major artery en route. Then, having fractured the spine in the sixth and seventh vertebrae, damaging the spinal cord, it lodged 5 cm (2 in) below his right shoulder blade in the muscles of his back. This corresponds with the angle and trajectory at which the ball was fired from the opposing French battleship.

Nelson stoically reported that he had difficulty breathing and felt a gush of blood inside his chest. Still conscious, he asked his valet to 'turn him on to his right side', which gave him scant relief. Nevertheless, the admiral remained conscious for a further three hours, mostly in terrible agony. Beatty wrote, 'The spinal injury by itself could have been mortal, but from it alone he could have survived 2–3 days although in miserable condition.' Beatty eventually removed the ball aboard the *Victory* before arriving in England in December 1805. While extricating the offending projectile he found 'a portion of the gold-lace and pad of the epaulette, together with a small piece of his Lordship's coat firmly attached to it'. Although Beatty's diagnosis and treatment were considered indisputable at the time, recent forensic neurosurgical analysis of Lord Nelson's fatal wound at Trafalgar reached a more thorough conclusion.

In medical jargon it is something along these lines: Blood loss from a torn pulmonary artery or from one of its branches, and/or compression of vital structures by a haemothorax, was neither the only nor the main cause of his death, considering that the bleeding was just moderate and that modern ballistics excludes a major vessel in the trajectory of the musket ball. Lord Nelson, hot at first and cold thereafter, paralyzed, with back pain and a weak arterial pulse, died mostly of and in spinal shock, following complete damage of the mid-thoracic spinal cord. The cord was transected at T6-7 by the passage of a ball shot by a French musketeer, resulting in loss/paralysis of all neurological activity below the level of the lesion, including motor, sensory, reflex and autonomic function. This prevented the body of the admiral, despite its youth, from compensating for the chest bleed, contributing to end-organ cellular dysfunction/death from tissue hypoperfusion.

During the epic Battle of Waterloo more than 6,000 wounded were taken to the farm of Mont St Jean, a place that first belonged to the Knight's Hospitallers, a few hundred yards behind the allied line. The British Army provided 180 surgeons at the Battle of Waterloo, roughly one for every 100 soldiers.

Lieutenant George Simmons of the 95th Rifles, who was treated at the farm, wrote: 'A good friend of mine instantly came to examine my wound. My breast was dreadfully swelled. He made a deep cut under the right pap, and dislodged from the breastbone a musket-ball. I was suffocating with the injury my lungs had sustained.'

Wellington described the battle as a 'Close run thing'. So chaotic was the situation on the day that the surgeons at Mont St Jean fully expected the French to break through at any moment, and had contingency plans to evacuate in the event. Cannonballs were already impacting the farm, causing much consternation. The wounded that could be moved were immediately evacuated to safety further north. Legend says that one of the few people to remain voluntarily was the farmer's wife, who insisted on staying to guard her chickens.

Lieutenant Simmons became rather agitated and demanded that a hospital sergeant tell him if he was going to be left at the farm. A fellow rifleman, Lieutenant Elliot Johnston, crawled over to comfort him with these noble words: 'George, do not swear at the fellow, we shall soon be happy, we have behaved like Englishmen.' Nevertheless, both men were eventually placed on horseback and led north. While convalescing in Brussels Simmons wrote a glowing report about his bedside attendant: 'My dear little nurse has never been ten minutes from me since I came to the house. For ten nights together she never went to bed, but laid her head on my pillow.'

Lieutenant Johnston was killed instantly when hit by a stray French cannonball bouncing up the cobbled road on which he was riding. Lieutenant Simmons made it out of the danger zone to Brussels but suffered excruciating pain, writing: 'The motion of the horse made the blood pump out, and the bones cut the flesh to a jelly.' At Brussels, he would be bled repeatedly both by the knife and by leeches. He made a full recovery against all the odds and died in 1858, aged 72.

Nearly all the men wounded in a limb had to endure amputation, as doctors had no other method of preventing gangrene or tetanus. The survival rate was calculated on the basis that one in three amputees had a chance of survival. Anaesthetics were unheard of at the time, and while many bore the agony with extraordinary fortitude there were also those who did not survive the shock of the operation. One audacious French soldier seized his amputated leg and tossed it in the air with a shout of 'Vive l'empereur'. Lord Fitzroy Somerset, Wellington's military secretary, was operated on by Dr John Gunning and was so unshaken that he called out, 'Hey! Don't carry away that arm till I've taken off my ring.'

John Haddy James of the 1st Life Guards remembered: 'The silent suffering of the greater part of the sufferers was a thing I shall not forget. When one considers the hasty surgery performed on such an occasion, the awful sights the men are witness to, knowing that their turn on that blood-soaked operating table is next, seeing the agony of an amputation, however swiftly performed, and the longer torture of a probing, then one realizes fully of what our soldiers are made.'

The surgeons accomplished wonders given the state of available medical science and the floods of men descending on them. One of their cruellest tasks, wrote William Gibney, 'was to be obliged to tell a dying soldier who had served his king and country well on that day, that his case was hopeless, more especially when he was unable to realize the same for himself, and then to pass on to another, where skill might avail'. He went on to say that 'The agony of some was so terrible, that they prayed to be killed outright than endure excruciating torture.'

There was actually an American at the momentous battle who also experienced the hell of Mont St Jean at close range. New Yorker Col. Sir William Howe De Lancey was a highly respected friend of the Iron Duke and remained in proximity to him on the day of his greatest triumph. On the afternoon of the battle, mounted on horseback and talking to Wellington, he was knocked clean from his horse when struck in the back by a spent cannonball. The initial impact broke eight ribs. While the battle raged, Lieutenant Colonel De Lancey Barclay of the 1st Foot Guards, an assistant adjutant general and Sir William's cousin, saw the event and ordered four soldiers to carry the wounded officer to the safety of a barn at Mont St Jean. After the battle, Wellington erroneously announced De Lancey's death in his dispatches. When the duke discovered his mistake, he went to Mont St Jean where De Lancey was being tended. Wellington told De Lancey of his error and even joked with his old friend, 'Why, De Lancey! You will know what your friends said of you after you were dead,' to which Sir William bravely replied, 'I hope I shall.' Despite attentive nursing by his bride of just two months, the stunningly beautiful Lady Magdalene Hall, De Lancey died a few days later.

Born in New York City in 1778, De Lancey was a member of one of the city's most powerful families. He was buried on 28 June 1815, in a cemetery in St Joose-ten-Noode, on the south side of the Chaussée de Louvain. In 1889, by order of Queen Victoria, De Lancey's remains, and those of other officers who fell at Waterloo, were moved to a massive monument in Evere, a suburb of Brussels near the present-day headquarters of NATO. For nearly two centuries, many assumed that De Lancey had died in the barn at Mont St Jean, due to its well-documented role as a British hospital during and after the battle. But doubts remained and other details of De Lancey's last days were shrouded in mystery. In 1999, in a corner of an attic, Lady Magdalene's great-great-great-grandson made a startling discovery. Inside a dust-covered trunk, he found the widowed bride's original diary, two portraits of young Magdalene and 40 hand-signed letters.

Magdalene had rushed from Antwerp to see De Lancey. Accompanied by a certain Mr Hay, she noted in her letters that she rode in a carriage through packed crowds of wounded, past fields filled with the dead from the battle that made their horses 'scream at the smell of corruption'. Magdalene describes her emotion as she waited to see whether her husband was still alive: 'How fervently and sincerely I resolved that if I saw him alive for one hour I never would repine! I had almost lost my recollection, with the excess of anxiety and suspense, when Mr Hay called out, "All's well; I have seen him. He expects you".'

She nursed Sir William for six days, until he 'gave a little gulp' and died. Magdalene visited her husband's grave near Brussels on 4 July 1815. 'That day, three months before, I was married.' Later that year, the widowed Lady De Lancey recorded her reminiscences in a journal, which was originally intended only for the eyes of her close friends and family. She may have felt the need to protect her reputation as a devoted and grieving wife, but malicious rumours circulated that she had been insufficiently remorseful after Waterloo, although it's more than possible she was just being stoic.

Charles Bell, a renowned surgeon, anatomist and artist who acquired a sound knowledge of gunshot wounds while volunteering as a surgeon during the Peninsular War, was present ten days after the Battle of Waterloo. He offered his services to the British Army upon arriving in Brussels and worked ceaselessly, often operating for up to 12 hours a day. He wrote, 'My clothes were stiff with blood and my arms powerless with the exertion of using my knife.'

Unfortunately, he was a better artist than he was a sawbones because 90 per cent of the wounded soldiers that underwent amputations in his charge didn't survive the ordeal. Nevertheless, the Edinburgh physician still made a number of meaningful contributions to military medicine by making accurate, ornate paintings of his studies from the battle, wherein he depicts his patients and their injuries in remarkable detail. The series provide a moving record of the horrific wounds dealt with by army surgeons in Wellington's army. As Chair of Anatomy at the Royal Academy, Bell was also a prolific author, and his experiences at Waterloo would go on to help future battlefield surgeons. His combined artistic, scientific and literary talents made him a particularly valuable guide to the realities of war. Bell's portraits of his patients describe not just their wounds and lacerations with anatomical accuracy but also their utter desolate, shocked or agonized expressions post-treatment, ten or 12 days after injury. So, he could paint and he could write – but if you encountered him after a bloody battle the best option was to get in another queue for another medic.

Charles Bell was a physician, an author and an artist who had been present at the Battle of Waterloo. A veritable 'jack of all trades'.

Letters to Bell from other surgeons also in charge of the patients emphasized the gruesome situations he had depicted. Surgeons witnessed wounds of the liver, bladder and head, and in some cases even worse scenarios. One surgeon wrote: 'Capt. Campbell was my only death, I would not be permitted to open the body, he died spitting pus and with a liver morosely distended.' But at least he provided a good subject for one of Bell's artworks.

CHAPTER FIVE

THIS NIGHTINGALE

For many, she is the feted 'Lady with the Lamp', the dedicated, incorruptible woman who cared for the British wounded in the Crimea. But Florence Nightingale was much more than a simple nurse. She was a complex, devious, ambitious woman whose modus operandi occasionally provoked more scorn than praise. Few people in medical history have been as praised and pilloried as Ms Nightingale.

The year was 1853, a time when Britannia ruled much more than just the waves, its empire stretching across the world and protected and maintained through violence, brutality, conquest and conflict. It was during this time of manic patriotism that a dubious alliance was formed between the British, the French, the Ottoman Turks and the Sardinians against the Russians (although the Italians joined the alliance for reasons best known to themselves). The end result of this unusual union of nations was the Crimean War.

It all began in 1853 when French Emperor Napoleon III, nephew of Napoleon Bonaparte, compelled the Ottoman Sultan Abdulmecid I to recognize France as the protector of the Christian peoples in Ottoman Palestine, which at that time comprised the whole eastern shore of the Mediterranean. This included the sizeable area of land we now know as Israel and Palestine, but also Lebanon and bits of Syria and Turkey were thrown in for good measure.

CHAPTER FIVE

When information of this erstwhile annexation reached the Russian tsar Nicholas I it was not well received. Russian troops were dispatched to Ottoman-administered territories in the Danubian provinces, in present-day Romania. This provoked Abdulmecid to promptly declare war on Russia. A surprise attack on Turkish ships in the Battle of Sinope ensued, which drew Britain and France into a war that would be fought on three fronts almost simultaneously. We will focus primarily here on the Crimean front, a conflict that entailed brutal sieges, suicidal charges and some mediocre if famous poetry.

Only a few weeks into the war it became apparent that more soldiers were succumbing to disease than to shrapnel, bullets, sabres and lances combined. Apart from being a logistical nightmare the war was also bringing to light the extreme deficiencies in providing for the care and treatment of wounded soldiers. It was time for Ms Florence Nightingale to don her lace apron and make an appearance. She became one of the most famous Victorian figures in history and is often depicted in a quasi-romantic role as the angel of mercy, tending the desperately ill soldiers by candlelight.

But despite her iconic status she remains a controversial figure that still inspires unadulterated praise from some and malicious scorn from others. Were her intentions genuinely altruistic or was she simply an ostentatious, media-hungry self-publicist? Morally corrupt Victorian Britain adored its heroes and viciously derided its villains. There wasn't a great deal of room to manoeuvre because British society rarely displayed objective ambiguity, but Florence may have provided the exception.

There is sufficient evidence to show that throughout her life she worked vigorously to improve the lives of the less fortunate in society. This often entailed being painfully obsequious to government organizations when the need suited her ambition. But she could be haughty, too, and has been criticized for her sometimes harsh bedside manner. In a burst of what may have been sibling rivalry, her sister Parthenope unflatteringly described Florence as, 'A shocking nurse. She has little or none of what is called charity or philanthropy, she is ambitious, very, and would like to regenerate the world. I wish she could be brought to see that it is the intellectual part that interests her, not the manual. Florence's interests were in the administrative, at which she was very adept, however she could be impatient with other people and was reported especially to have not worked well with other women.'

The unpublished letters of one of Florence Nightingale's contemporaries paint an equally disturbing portrait of a woman guilty of blithe, hypocritical misogyny, and as being domineering, bossy, bloody-minded and self-promoting. This directly contradicts those who regarded Florence as being sweet-natured, courageous and altruistic. It's also entirely possible that some of the more scathing accounts were based on pure jealousy because Florence was indeed a very assertive, independent-minded person, which was in direct contrast to the demure, shrinking violet roles imposed on Victorian women in that very male-dominated, hypocritical society. Her attitude alone would have incited the rancour of the starch-collared males, who didn't need much provocation in order to start harrumphing.

She was raised in a fairly affluent upper-middle-class family, and was fortunate that in the patriarchal society of the day her father was quite a forward thinker who, in contrast to his male peers, extolled the virtues of women's education. But despite her education and her father's encouragement Florence remained encumbered by a domineering family and struggled to find true fulfilment in her life. This left her frustrated, unable to use her undoubted intelligence and unassailable energy. On several occasions she was driven to the edge of mental breakdown.

In 1850 she wrote, 'My present life is suicide. I have no desire but to die.' Believing she heard the voice of God calling her to his service, she rejected marriage and decided that her true destiny lay in nursing. Her family vociferously opposed this, claiming it was an occupation entirely unsuitable for a lady of her standing. Their objections were a little assuaged when Florence was appointed superintendent at the Hospital for Invalid Gentlewomen on Harley Street.

In late 1853 as the British paraded in the mellow fruitfulness of autumn, dispatches and newspaper articles began to circulate reporting on the deplorable conditions wounded and ill British soldiers had to endure in the Crimean War. Many a Victorian household witnessed the father spluttering his Earl Grey at the breakfast table over the latest reports from the Russian front.

William Howard Russell of *The Times* wrote many of these initial dispatches. He described in gory detail the appalling conditions in military hospitals and the terrible suffering of the wounded and sick troops who languished there. Apart from invoking a public outcry, Howard's articles prompted his newspaper to launch an appeal on behalf of these unfortunate soldiers.

On 14 October 1854 Florence formally requested and was granted permission to leave her job in the Harley Street hospital, in order to lead a private expedition to the Crimea. The Minister of War, Sidney Herbert, had already written to Florence kindly requesting her to go to the Crimea on behalf of the government and take responsibility for the introduction of female nurses into those deplorable hospitals.

In 1854, Florence and 38 other female volunteers were deployed to the Ottoman Empire. They travelled to Marseilles and boarded a ship called the *Vectis*, arriving at the Scutari barracks hospital in Constantinople, Turkey, on 4 November 1854. Unfortunately, they didn't arrive to brass bands and bunting as most army doctors were fiercely opposed to women working in their facilities. The nurses were initially allocated menial tasks that restricted their activities to sewing, laundry duties and checking the stores. This condescending attitude of the doctors changed radically after the devastating Battle of Inkerman.

British Lieutenant-General Hamley described the fighting: 'This extraordinary battle closed with no final charge nor victorious advance on the one side, no desperate stand nor tumultuous flight on the other. The Russians, when hopeless of success, seemed to melt from the lost field.'

Exhausted English and French regiments surveyed the carnage of a field strewn with bloodied casualties. The battle culminated in a stunning victory for the British Army even though they were outnumbered five to one throughout much of the fighting. It was here that the first mention of the 'thin red line' was mentioned. The tally for the Brits was quite high; they sustained 597 killed and roughly 1,860 wounded. Alexander Kinglake, a popular historian and travel writer of the day, somehow obtained the official casualty returns for the battle. According to him allied casualties amounted to 2,573 British, of whom 635 were killed, and 1,800 French, of

Florence Nightingale was a force to be reckoned with. After a particularly bumpy start, she paved the way for future nurses.

whom 175 were killed. Russia lost 3,286 souls within a total (including men taken prisoner) of 11,959 casualties.

This was the proverbial turning point when doctors were reluctantly compelled to ask Florence Nightingale and her nurses if they could lend more practical assistance to deal with the situation. Appalled by the conditions at the hospital, Florence wrote an urgent plea to *The Times* asking for food supplies, desperately needed medicine and the means to better the deplorable conditions of the camp. The requested supplies were quickly dispatched and concerted efforts were made to clean up the hospital. Florence began making improvements to the cleanliness of the hospitals and began providing the soldiers with clean clothes and sheets. She also worked to upgrade the hygienic demands of the buildings. With the help of a chef called Alexis Soyer, she also improved the soldiers' diet by providing them with healthier and more nutritious food.

It's fair to say that she initially found her new authority quite disorientating because she adopted an almost matriarchal approach to the patients in her care, referring to them as 'my children'. Indeed, to those men far from home Florence and her nurses were a great comfort.

It was all to little avail. Although Florence understood some of the medical needs and necessary hygiene requirements, she remained strangely intransigent regarding the true cause of most of the soldiers' deaths, which were due to the disastrous sanitary arrangements at the facility. During her first winter at Scutari, 4,077 soldiers perished from illnesses such as typhus, typhoid, cholera and dysentery. Ten times more soldiers succumbed to these illnesses than from battle wounds. Conditions at the hospital were potentially fatal to the men that Nightingale was attempting to nurse. Being packed like sardines in an unventilated building that had been built above defective sewers didn't help either.

Nightingale's early years were undoubtedly responsible for her streak of steely ruthlessness. She was a slender, graceful person who managed her image with all the acumen of a multinational PR rep. She could turn on the charm and flutter the eyelids when required, but this was a feint. Florence possessed an almost maniacal resolve. In her defence, she also possessed one of the great administrative minds of the nineteenth century.

Nightingale speciously continued to attribute responsibility for the high number of deaths at Scutari to inadequate nutrition and insufficient supplies. Ironically, she refused to acknowledge the main reason so many died, preferring to rely on her own opinions. As a result, the death rate in Florence's camp was higher than at any other hospital facility.

It was only when Florence eventually returned to Britain that she began to change her mind. After collecting evidence to present before the Royal Commission on the Health of the Army, Florence reached the painful conclusion that most of the soldiers at her hospital had indeed perished due to bad sanitation, exacerbated by her ignorance. Even if she did provide cleaner surroundings and greater comfort she had indirectly caused many, many deaths. It is completely true, however, that Florence famously walked the wards every night holding a Turkish lantern. This led to the soldiers affectionately giving Florence her famous nickname. But it's equally true that the legendary Lady with the Lamp was actually more of a Grim Reaper in the Crimea.

In the long run Florence had an incredibly positive effect on the care of wounded and ill soldiers in the British Army, but it had been a tragic learning curve. Her conduct and genuine attempt to improve conditions for soldiers served to highlight other equally debilitating health problems that could arise due to inadequate sanitary arrangements. Nevertheless, Florence Nightingale was indeed an innovator, and remains an iconic figure both roundly pilloried and venerated from all angles. She has been accused by some of conceit, arrogance and ignorance, but it remains irrefutable that she did a lot of good by reducing unnecessary deaths in the army during peacetime, before turning her attention to nursing and introducing sanitary concepts into hospitals. So, in many ways she was indeed a pioneer – but there was still a long and painful road ahead.

CHAPTER SIX

THE EXTRAORDINARY MARY SEACOLE

Imagine for a moment lying wounded on a foreign field while the terrifying dissonance of battle fills the air. In the midst of all the blood, chaos and mayhem you see a rather rotund, garishly attired black lady riding towards you at a steady pace, accompanied by two heavily laden mules. Moreover, she doesn't appear to be unduly worried. Suddenly, she releases a thunderous postern blast, unceremoniously dismounts her overladen mule and approaches you wearing a big, comforting smile. This bumptious, adorable lady is Mrs Mary Seacole and you're in luck. Now you have a chance.

Florence Nightingale scored a serious PR victory for her work in the Crimea, and in burnishing her own reputation she made little reference to one of the nurses who contributed greatly to the welfare of those same British troops. The sight of this gregarious, jolly woman arriving with her remedies was a mental and physical panacea for any wounded soldier on a foreign battlefield. In her lifetime Mary Seacole (1805–81) achieved celebrity status among the volatile Victorian British public who, thanks to articles written by numerous journalists, were well aware of her compassion, skill and courage.

Many contemporary historians believe that Mary's contribution to the health and welfare of soldiers in the Crimea far exceeded that of Florence Nightingale. Once more the image may have exceeded the ability, and attitudes towards Mary were on occasion painfully patronizing, but it couldn't detract from the good that this amazing woman did during her life.

Mary Seacole, or 'Mother Seacole' as she affectionately became known to the troops, was born in Kingston, Jamaica, in 1805 and christened Mary Jane Grant. Her father James Grant was a hard-drinking Scottish officer posted there as part of the British military contingent. Her hugely influential mother, also named Mary was a creole (a person of mixed European and black descent), and a skilful exponent of traditional Jamaican herbal remedies and medicines. She ran Blundell Hall, reputedly one of the finest hotels in Kingston, where she cared for invalid soldiers and their wives. This was the world that Mary Seacole was born into. Her education in medicine came mainly from her mother but benefited from other influences. The authorities legally classified her as a mulatto, a person born of bi-racial parentage. Here the waters get a little muddy as, technically, she was regarded as a quadroon, a person with one bi-racial parent and one white parent. Many years later Seacole wrote, 'My father was a soldier, of an old Scotch family; and to him I often trace my affection for a camp-life, and my sympathy with what I have heard my friends call "the pomp, pride, and circumstances of glorious war".'

As a soldier, James Grant's duty was to protect this lucrative British island against foreign invasion. The island had belonged to Britain since 10 May 1655, when Admiral William Penn and General Robert Venables had forced Spain to relinquish possession. At the time of Seacole's birth, Jamaica was emerging as one of the many proverbial jewels in Britain's imperial crown as the world's leading exporter of sugar. Jamaica's black population was known as the 'Maroons' and was originally imported as slave labour from Africa by the British to work on the sugar plantations. In 1800, just five years before Seacole was born, the island's 300,000 slaves outnumbered the white population by ten to one and the British authorities had been forced to contend with a few uprisings.

The bumptious, unflappable Mary Seacole was always a welcome sight anywhere on the battle-field. She probably saved more lives than her white counterpart Ms Nightingale.

Some British soldiers regarded a posting to the Caribbean early in the nineteenth century as a death sentence. This was mainly due to its various epidemics of yellow fever, cholera, malaria and typhoid. This reduced the effectiveness and numbers of British soldiers stationed there to such an extent that they were compelled to recruit former slaves as troops. In 1807, the Mutiny Act was introduced, which granted freedom to all black men who served in the British armed forces. These men received the same pay and rations as white soldiers. They were also supposed to be subject to the same punishments, but the introduction of the Act surreptitiously introduced a new form of inequality. Black soldiers joining the British West India regiments had to sign up for life, in contrast to their white counterparts who joined up for seven-year terms. It looked good on paper but in reality there was still extensive racism among the ranks.

Mary Grant married an Englishman, Edwin Horatio Hamilton Seacole, on 10 November 1836 in Kingston, Jamaica. Edwin was a naval officer and was reputed to be the illegitimate son of Horatio Nelson and his mistress, Lady Hamilton. Mary Seacole's last will and testament contradicted this claim by stating that Edwin was not the illegitimate offspring but the 'Godson' of Nelson. He was the adopted son of Edwin Thomas Seacole, a local 'surgeon, apothecary' and male midwife, who raised the boy as his own.

Edwin never enjoyed a particularly healthy life and he died in 1844, which was coincidentally the same year that Mary's mother also passed. Mary never remarried, preferring to dedicate herself to managing her mother's hotel and, eventually, frontline nursing. She treated victims in the cholera epidemic of 1850 that claimed the lives of over 32,000 Jamaicans. Her efficacious treatment of patients during this crisis proved beneficial in later years. She wrote: 'I had gained a reputation as a skilful nurse and doctress, and my house was always full of invalid officers and their wives from Newcastle, or the adjacent Up-Park Camp. Sometimes I had a naval or military surgeon under my roof, from whom I never failed to glean instruction, given, when they learned my love for their profession, with a readiness and kindness I am never likely to forget.'

During her lifetime Seacole travelled extensively and, on one occasion, in 1852, she was travelling between Panama and the United States and spending time in the company of American traders. As she left the dinner table she overheard an American say, 'God bless the best yaller woman he ever made. If we could bleach her by any means we would and make her acceptable in any company as she deserves to be.' This infuriated Seacole, who wrote in her autobiography, 'I must say that I don't appreciate your friend's kind wishes with respect to my complexion. If it had been as dark as a nigger's, I should have been just as happy and useful, and as much respected by those whose respect I value: and as to his offer of bleaching me, I should, even if it were practicable, decline it without any thanks.'

She was reputed to have been a fiercely loyal patriot and in her lifetime made a number of journeys to the United Kingdom. Unfortunately, her loyalty and love for the country wasn't always reciprocated. It was during one of these visits that Seacole heard about the Crimean War. She was so moved by the distressing newspaper articles that she made applications to the War Office, British medical authorities, the army medical department and the Secretary of War to be allowed to go to the Crimea and tend to the desperately sick and wounded men. She was promptly refused and turned away at every juncture. Some claim that she even attempted to join Florence Nightingale's group of nurses. She didn't meet Nightingale at the time but it's alleged that one of her assistants refused to allow Mary to join the team. Deeply disappointed at the rejections, Mary observed, 'Was it possible, that American prejudices against colour had taken root here? Did these ladies shrink from accepting my aid because my blood flowed beneath a somewhat duskier skin than theirs?'

No shrinking violet, Mary protested, pointing out that she had extensive experience, excellent references and even knew some of the soldiers and regiments, having nursed them while they had been stationed in Jamaica. Her eventual value to the soldiers in the Crimea could to some extent be attributed to her wide knowledge of the pathology of cholera, which she had contracted and recovered from. Undaunted, Mary made a further attempt to get to the Crimea when she applied for sponsorship and was flatly refused by the Crimean Fund, a charity founded by public subscription to support the wounded in Crimea. Despite all the adversity, she continued to explore ways to get to the warzone where, despite her detractors, she was convinced that she would be able to do some good.

It was quite serendipitous, therefore, that Thomas Day, a relative of her deceased husband, was planning to go to the Crimea on business. After some discussion she agreed to establish a limited company with him that would become known as Seacole and Day.

Finally, on 27 January 1855, Seacole secured a passage to Constantinople on board the Dutch ship *Hollander*. Armed with a letter of recommendation, she met and had a brief conversation with Florence Nightingale at the famous Scutari Army hospital in Turkey, which she refers to in her autobiography:

'In half an hour's time I am admitted to Miss Nightingale's presence. A slight figure, in the nurses' dress; with a pale, gentle, and withal firm face, resting lightly in the palm of one white hand, while the other supports the elbow, a position which gives to her countenance a keen inquiring expression, which is rather marked. Standing thus in repose, and yet keenly observant, the greatest sign of impatience at any time a slight, perhaps unwitting motion of the firmly planted right foot was Florence Nightingale, that Englishwoman whose name shall never die, but sound like music on the lips of British men until the hour of doom. She has read Dr. F—'s letter, which lies on the table by her side, and asks, in her gentle but eminently practical and business-like way, "What do you want, Mrs Seacole – anything that we can do for you? If it lies in my power, I shall be very happy."

'So I tell her of my dread of the night journey by caicque, and the improbability of my finding the *Hollander* in the dark; and, with some diffidence, threw myself upon the hospitality of Scutari, offering to nurse the sick for the night. Now unfortunately, for many reasons, room even for one in Scutari Hospital was at that time no easy matter to find; but at last a bed was discovered to be unoccupied at the hospital washerwomen's quarters.'

Seacole stayed just one night at Scutari before taking another ship the following day across the Black Sea to the Crimean battle zone. When she arrived in the Crimea she promptly set up a hotel, Spring Hill. Others

Nightingale's choice of location for her hospital at Scutari during the Crimean War may have done considerably more harm than good, but it provided a valuable lesson.

referred to it as 'Mrs Seacole's hut'. The first floor served as a restaurant, while the second floor was requisitioned as a treatment area similar to a field hospital. She financed her operation by selling supplies while serving meals and copious amounts of alcohol. She then used her profits for the care of the ill and injured. Bear in mind that this woman was 50 years old at the time and quite portly, but despite her age and physical constitution she maintained an irrepressible dynamism and endearing nature that acted like a virtual magnet to soldiers far from home. It didn't take long for the name of Mother Seacole to spread through the entire British Army. Higher officials referred to her condescendingly as a 'sutler', someone who follows the army and sells provisions to the troops, but she did more, much more than just that.

Because she wasn't officially attached to any organization during the Crimean War Mary had complete freedom of movement, which would have been denied to Florence Nightingale and her staff. In the Crimea

Seacole adopted a strict routine, treating those with medical conditions each morning and then, accompanied by two mules, one carrying medicaments and the other food and wine, she would travel to the frontlines to treat casualties on site. On a number of occasions, she tended wounded men from both sides while the battle was still raging.

William Howard Russell, special correspondent of *The Times*, wrote in 1856: 'In the hour of their illness, these men have found a kind and successful physician, who doctors and cures all manner of men with extraordinary success. She is always in attendance near the battlefield to aid the wounded and has earned many a poor fellow's blessing.' Whenever she approached the frontlines Mary Seacole's presence would have been immediately acknowledged – not least because she insisted on wearing highly conspicuous, brightly coloured clothing, even as the bullets and cannonballs flew around her.

Financially, her Crimean venture left much to be desired. In 1857 she returned to London, suffering from ill health and bankruptcy. Her left foot was inflamed, possibly due to gout, so it wouldn't have been entirely wrong to describe her as the 'Lady with the limp'. Thanks to her outstanding service during the Crimean War, the British press rallied and advertised her pitiful plight. Many people donated to a fund for her and, even though Florence Nightingale was somewhat critical of Seacole's work, it was alleged that she secretly contributed to the fund. Later that year and at the insistence of those close to her she wrote her autobiography, titled somewhat ostentatiously *Wonderful Adventures of Mrs Seacole in Many Lands*. Unlike most budding authors her fame was such that she had no problem finding a publisher. The ensuing book sold remarkably well and she lived out her remaining years in relative comfort. Mary Seacole died following a cerebral haemorrhage in London on 14 May 1881 and was sadly soon forgotten.

Since 1981, on the anniversary of her death a wreath-laying ceremony is held at her grave and in 2005 Penguin Classics reprinted her book. The bicentenary of Seacole's birth was celebrated with the unveiling of a lost painting of her at the National Portrait Gallery in London. A fundraising campaign in her name raised over half a million pounds and led to the unveiling of a beautiful statue of Mary Seacole, in the grounds of St

Thomas' Hospital, London. This memorial statue is believed to be the UK's first in honour of a black woman.

Her methods of treatment may have been regarded as unorthodox by the Victorian medical establishment, and many claimed that she profited from the British Army, but she rightfully earned her place as one of the most famous nurses in history. Mary's memory lives on. God bless her.

CHAPTER SEVEN

AMERICAN CIVIL WAR NURSES

I mprovements in the care that British soldiers received during the latter part of the Crimean War, and the famous exploits of Florence Nightingale and the British Sanitary Commission were well known to American authorities. But that does not mean they were well-prepared for what they would have to deal with on the outbreak of the American Civil War.

The conflict began in 1861, the violent manifestation of a long-running disagreement between the slave-holding southern states and their abolitionist northern counterparts. There was much more to the American Civil War, of course, with a major sub-plot being the power that individual states claimed of self-rule against the over-riding authority of the federal government in Washington DC.

The catalyst was the election of Abraham Lincoln as President of the United States of America in November 1860. He had stood on a policy of opposition to the further expansion of slavery in the United States. After taking office he also rejected the idea that any individual state could unilaterally secede from the union – as some slave-owning states had proposed, believing that Lincoln wanted ultimately to abolish slavery completely.

When Confederate batteries took aim and fired on Fort Sumter on 12 April 1861, forcing its surrender, war became inevitable. Encouraged by shrewd politicians and jingoistic headlines printed by morally opaque newspaper proprietors, both sides soon escalated the conflict. President Lincoln, who had only been in office since 6 November 1860, wasted no time calling on the states to provide the Union Army with 75,000 volunteers. As more states joined the opposing Confederacy, its armies swelled accordingly. They would all soon experience terrible fear, loss and suffering on an unprecedented scale. Most of them would march into the withering maelstrom of lead and shrapnel, largely oblivious to the political aspirations each side represented and ignorant of the grim reality of mid-nineteenth-century warfare, assured by the knowledge that God was on their side.

The result was a fight for the very survival of the United States of America, for control of the idea of what a nation should be. It set brother against brother, community against community, and claimed the lives of more than 600,00 people. Even today its legacy lays like a scar across the body politic of America.

On a practical, medical level the civil war presented the armies of both sides with considerable problems to overcome. We have several sources from the Union side that show in vivid detail how those challenges were addressed – not least by some remarkable women driven by fate to do their bit on the battlefield and beyond for their fallen countrymen.

The first thing the US Sanitary Commission had to deal with once the war began was organize how to provide the Union Army with medical supplies and equipment. Many of these had been purchased from donations, and the Commission had no official authority to direct how these supplies and equipment should be used. Furthermore, the US Medical Department managed to start the conflict on the wrong foot. The first major battle of the war, fought at Bull Run in Manassas, Virginia, on 21 July 1861, highlighted how woefully unprepared the Union Army was from a medical standpoint. There was no properly organized triage procedure, while the provision of medical assistance to battlefield casualties was haphazard at best. Fortunately, at Bull Run casualty figures were relatively small compared with future battles, with 481 Northern soldiers killed (and 1,011 wounded) and 387 Southern fatalities (with 1,582 wounded).

The nature of most of the injuries at this battle, apart from the inevitable shrapnel, were the result of soldiers being shot with the 'Minié' ball. This was a slow muzzle-velocity 0.58-caliber bullet made from soft lead invented by the French officer Claude-Etienne Minié in 1849. It flattened on impact to create a wound that expanded as the bullet burrowed deeper into tissue. It shattered bone above and below impact and rarely exited. Its shape and slow movement caused bits of clothing, skin and bacteria to infiltrate the wound, significantly raising the risk of infection. The majority of gunshot wounds occurred in the upper and lower extremities, which often resulted in amputations, but the fatality rate from these wounds was relatively low. Three out of every four surgical procedures performed during the war were amputations. Only 18 per cent of wounds were to the abdomen, though these were more likely to be fatal due to intestinal perforation in the pre-antibiotic era.

Many medical problems were encountered at Bull Run. For a start there was no official military ambulance corps, though there were private ambulance carts present. Many civilians that had congregated to witness the battle fled when the first shots were fired. Unfortunately, some of them drove these ambulances. Of the ambulances that were left behind by hastily fleeing civilians, these were in turn requisitioned by healthy troops in a hurry to make a strategic withdrawal from the battlefield. Consequently, not a single wounded soldier was taken back to the safety of Washington DC in an ambulance. Tragically, wounded soldiers were left on the rain-soaked battlefield for days. In addition, Surgeon General Clement Finley did not order medical supplies until after the battle was over. In 1862, 33-year-old William Hammond replaced Finley, and he initiated some reforms that improved things. For example, he set about militarizing the medical care a wounded soldier could receive. The wounded were moved from field stations to field hospitals, to division or corps hospitals, then to hospitals in major army centres in nearby cities.

If a battle produced more casualties than regimental facilities could handle, a temporary field hospital manned by regimental surgeons was established. Brigade and division hospitals were sometimes set up to consolidate regimental hospitals. The Medical Department reinstituted the general hospital in the major cities of the north to cope with incoming sick and wounded. There was no shortage of volunteers to work in these hospitals, the first of which was established in Washington DC. Improved

Savage Station, Union Field Hospital, 27 June 1862.

management of the medical facilities was augmented by the staff of surgeons, nurses and cooks.

During the American Civil War, Louisa May Alcott, who went on to write *Little Women*, worked for a short time as a nurse in one of these facilities. Alcott had no formal training and was no Florence Nightingale by any stretch of the imagination, but on 11 December 1862 she went to the Union hospital in Georgetown, outside Washington DC, to volunteer her services. She would later relate her experiences in her book *Hospital Sketches* (1863), which tells the story of a bedside army nurse.

In retrospect Alcott's wasn't a particularly substantial contribution because she only lasted for about six weeks, but it was long enough to provide her with inspiration and vital information for some of her future literary works. The real credit for any involvement in the war should be attributed more to her family than to the author herself. The Alcott family maintained a strongly humanitarian stance throughout this turbulent period in American history by providing a safe house for the revered Underground Railroad that assisted former slaves in escaping to safety in the north.

Despite her glaring lack of practical experience, Dorothea Dix, Superintendent of Army Nurses for the Union Army, accepted Alcott into service. Paradoxically, Dix also had no formal training as a nurse. It was rather her tenacity and exceptional organizational skills that impressed Secretary of War, Simon Cameron and Acting Surgeon General D. C. Wood into appointing her. This gave Dix the authority to select and assign women nurses to general or permanent military hospitals. No nurse could be employed in such hospitals without her sanction and approval, except in cases of urgent need. However, the criteria regarded as acceptable for this work by Ms Dix wasn't really academic or stringent. Her prime requirements were that her nurses be sober-minded, and preferably over 30. Candidates whom she deemed 'flighty', or attractive women, or those who wore stylish clothing and jewellery were considered highly inappropriate. They could distract the wounded, she thought.

Alcott's personal experience caring for sick family members before she went to DC did indeed prove useful when she was caring for wounded soldiers. Her first impressions of Georgetown Hospital must have been a shock to the system. It was an intrinsically unhealthy place to be a patient. Advances in the technology of warfare had created devastating weapons capable of inflicting horrific injuries. Unfortunately, advances in medical science had not kept pace.

Surgeons and nurses at that time had scant knowledge of bacterial infections, so many surgical procedures were performed without even the most rudimentary preparations, such as using soap and water or disinfectant. Georgetown Hospital was a humid, rancid-smelling hovel, inadequately supplied, overcrowded, chaotic and completely unsanitary. Preventable diseases such as typhoid and dysentery were rampant due to poor knowledge of epidemiology. Civil war army nursing was not for the faint-hearted or reticent; therefore Nurse Alcott would have been required to assist with torturous surgical procedures along with having to tend unsightly wounds, and alleviate the suffering of those who were dying painful, protracted deaths.

Just a few days after Nurse Alcott arrived at Georgetown there was a huge arrival of wounded Union soldiers. These were the casualties incurred when General Robert E. Lee led the Confederate Army to victory at the Battle of Fredericksburg that had involved almost 200,000 troops. As the wounded poured in, Alcott recoiled at the utter magnitude of human suffering the under-provisioned staff was expected to contend with. She was so shocked that at first she hid behind a pile of clothing, emerging only after she had composed herself. Then she got to work washing away blood and filth.

If it hadn't been for Dorothea Dix, America would have lost a future literary heroine.

At that time female nurses were considered a bit of a novelty among the ranks and this frequently caused altercations when changing dressings or bathing. Alcott appears to have adapted well and applied her infectious sense of humour to alleviate potentially embarrassing situations. This gift for communication would culminate in her literary work and inspire the resoundingly successful, semi-autobiographical novel *Little Women*.

Alcott contracted typhoid pneumonia in January 1863. Physicians attempted to treat the symptoms using analgesics and quinine. However, some physicians prescribed calomel for typhoid fever, which had the potential to cause mercury poisoning in many of the patients. Alcott's condition was regarded as so serious that Dorothea Dix sent for her father, who took her back home to New England. While recovering she appeared to display clear symptoms of what we would today call post-traumatic stress disorder (PTSD). Although she survived the disease, the enduring effects of being treated by calomel ruined Alcott's health. The remaining years of her life were blighted by recurrent pain, weakness and neurological problems. Despite this, she had been stirred by her experiences and possessed both the skill and the literary acumen to relate them to others.

Louisa May Alcott's boss at the facility in Georgetown, Dorothea Lynde Dix, had already been widely acknowledged among the medical community of the day as a crusader and reformer. Despite her lack of medical experience and qualifications, her dedication to duty was beyond reproach. She and the rest of the medical services, north and south, were facing unprecedented numbers of troops to deal with. Before the outbreak of the civil war the United States had maintained an army of between 20,000 to 25,000 men. Except in the case of the Mexican War of 1846–8, no authority in the country had ever coped with the problem of dealing with the medical care of forces larger than just a few regiments. Plus, army nursing was regarded as a wholly male domain.

After the outbreak of hostilities Dix effectively convinced cynical military officials that women were perfectly capable of nursing, and on the basis of this she personally recruited 2,000 women and formed the first Army Nursing Corps. Women volunteered their services on both sides of the Mason-Dixon line, but they were for the vast majority unqualified and totally inexperienced for the tasks they were about to face. Dix was often at loggerheads with military officials and when it suited she blatantly ignored military orders. It's an indisputable fact that army nursing care improved substantially under her supervision. She could on occasion be a little tyrannical, earning the nickname Dragon Dix, but she took good care of the nurses who laboured in the most terrible conditions. She even took measures to obtain vital health care supplies from private agencies when the government was not willing to provide them.

Dix was nearly 60 at the time of her appointment and not in the best of health. Her constitution had suffered malaria, long, punishing hours of work and pulmonary weakness. Throughout the previous decades she had operated single-handedly, planning her own projects, taking her own advice and pressing on, unhindered by the opinions of others as she strove to improve conditions in prisons and mental asylums. Here was a woman reinforced by her own towering idealism, by her thirst for organizational perfection and discipline – precisely the qualities needed for the job in hand.

So many wounded and sick soldiers flowed into Washington after the Battle of Bull Run that Dix's hospitals couldn't accommodate them all. She quickly requisitioned more buildings and converted them into hospitals to meet the high demand. When she discovered that the Union troops didn't have sufficient ambulances, she purchased one with her own money and dispatched it to Manassas. She also took steps to amend the gender pay imbalance. At the time male nurses were paid $20.50 a month and received rations, clothing and housing; all of Dix's nurses were unpaid volunteers. When they discovered their male counterparts were receiving so many financial and material concessions from the government there was some unrest. Dix realized that unless something was done she would lose many of her nurses. She applied to the government and achieved a victory when they agreed to provide female nurses with food, transportation and housing. They also agreed to pay the nurses 40 cents per day. Thanks to this, nursing numbers increased. This is where Dix shone brightly. She was a persuasive and demanding campaigner with both the intelligence and experience to effectively achieve her goals.

Dix also possessed the necessary empathy with human suffering that had been the spine of her long and wonderful philanthropic career until the outbreak of war. Once confronted with the massive task of caring for hundreds of wounded men she became involved in sharp altercations with prominent medical officials and regimental surgeons. She wanted to be both the avenging and guardian angel for the wounded in her care. Some of her friends claimed that she raised the bar way too high for anyone to meet her standards and failed to take due account of human nature. Although the qualifications required to work for Dix were loose, the aptitude and mental ability she demanded from her staff was great. Throughout those four long years of war she never took a day's leave herself. She worked ceaselessly, organizing bands of nurses, inspecting hospitals and meticulously reporting any cases of neglect or abuse. It was her direct capacity to reprimand offenders and praise those she felt worthy that made her name salutary.

One of her most debilitating characteristics though was her incapacity to fully understand the intricate logistics of full-on warfare. Her initial inability to deal with the constant stream of hundreds of tons of hospital supplies arriving in Washington DC was a detriment to the army. She had neither the adequate provision of storehouses nor the necessary means of distribution to amend the situation. The authorities eventually stepped in to assist but it took a while before the machinery of organization effectively kicked in. Dix's dedication was irrefutable.

At the end of the war Dix was personally asked by Secretary of War Edwin M. Stanton what kind of title or gift she would like to receive from a grateful nation. She had only one request, to be given the flags of her country – although in truth she never expected to get them. But, shortly after her conversation with Stanton she received the following letter:

'WAR DEPARTMENT, WASHINGTON CITY,

'December 3, 1866. Order in Relation to the Services of Miss Dix. In token and acknowledgment of the inestimable services rendered by Miss Dorothea L. Dix for the Care, Succor, and Relief of the Sick and Wounded Soldiers of the United States on the Battlefield, in Camps and Hospitals during the recent War, and of her benevolent and diligent labours and devoted efforts to whatever might contribute to their comfort and welfare, it is ordered that a Stand of Arms of the United States National Colors be presented to Miss Dix.

'EDWIN M. STANTON, Secretary of War'

Dix acknowledged the honour in a heartfelt letter:

'To GENERAL E. D. TOWNSEND. ALBANY, N. Y., January 25, 1867.

'Dear Sir, I am just in receipt of your letter of the 14th, and acknowledge with the deep emotion of a patriotic heart my sense of the honor conferred by the presentation through you from the Secretary of War of a Stand of the United States Colors. No greater distinction could have been conferred on me, and the value of this gift is greatly enhanced by the quiet manner in which it is bestowed.

'Respectfully, D. L. Dix.'

Dorothea Lynde Dix was a pioneer, a reformer who applied herself heart and soul to her campaigning work. Her contribution to the civil war pales by comparison to the reforms she achieved concerning the improvement of care of the mentally ill in America. Thanks to her untiring efforts and the depth of her compassion for her cause, the first insane asylums were created. She never stopped campaigning, only stopping when ill health caught up with her. Dorothea Dix died in New Jersey on 17 July 1887.

Another woman who made an incredible contribution to health care in the American Civil War and beyond was Clara Barton.

It's difficult to summarize the work and achievements of one of the most distinguished and memorable women of her day. She was an educator, a patent clerk, a nurse and the founder of the American Red Cross. The youngest of six children, Clarissa Harlowe Barton was born on Christmas Day in 1821, in North Oxford, Massachusetts. She was the daughter of a farmer, a Freemason who supported the abolitionist movement and was a keen advocate of the importance of education. Her mother was an active women's rights campaigner. In her lifetime Clara became known as the 'Angel of the Battlefield'. She independently organized facilities and secured medicine and supplies for casualties during some of the fiercest battles of that terrible war. Her efforts saved the lives of many men wounded in the Union Army at the battles of Cedar Mountain, Bull Run, Chantilly, Antietam, Fredericksburg, Hilton Head, the Wilderness and Petersburg.

She began her career as a teacher and after 12 successful years in the profession was contracted to open America's first free school in Bordentown, New Jersey, in 1852. After only one year as head teacher the authorities were persuaded to fund a new school building to the tune of $4,000, but there was a catch. It wasn't thought that the position of school head was suitable employment for a woman. Much to Clara's dismay a man was hired to replace her. If this wasn't bad enough, he was paid twice her salary. After suffering what can only be described as a nervous breakdown, Clara handed in her notice and left.

In February 1854 she applied for and secured a position as clerk in the Patent Office in Washington DC that was run by the Superintendent of Patents, Charles Mason. It's entirely possible that she was the first regularly appointed female civil servant in this entirely male domain. Her annual salary of $1,400 was equal with that of male clerks. This aroused jealousy, suspicion and a lot of discomforting verbal abuse from her chauvinistic male colleagues who derided Clara for her abolitionist opinions, among other things. Growing discontent by the government employees forced Clara to accept a lesser position as a copyist. She remained in that position until President Buchanan was elected in 1857. In his inaugural address, Buchanan referred to the contentious territorial issue of slavery as 'happily, a matter of but little practical importance'. He actively supported the theory that states and territories had a right to self-determination regarding the increasingly divisive slavery issue. When the Buchanan administration began eradicating anti-slavery sympathizers from the civil service in 1857 Clara was dismissed, but only two years later she was recalled to apply her knowledge and expertise. By this time the country was beginning to feel the pinch of an impending economic recession. President Buchanan's attempt to appease all ended up pleasing none, so there was little fear of him being re-elected.

Clara's patriotic sentiments were reflected in a sentence taken from a private letter she sent to her niece, Mrs Vassall. Its contents were to prove ominously correct: 'I think the city will be attacked within the next 60 days. If it must be, let it come, and when there is no longer a soldier's arm to raise the Stars and Stripes above our Capitol, may God give strength to mine.'

Clara Barton was right there at the beginning of the war. On 15 April, the state of Massachusetts dispatched four regiments to Washington in the Union cause. One of these, the 6th Regiment, was passing through Baltimore when they became the target of a 10,000-strong raging mob. Four soldiers ended up dead, while a further 30 suffered lighter wounds. Despite the opposition they managed to board the train to Washington DC. When they arrived, Lincoln told them that if they had not come to his aid that night, Washington DC would have been in the hands of the rebels before the morning. As the troops disembarked, Clara was there with other volunteer nurses to receive them and attend to their wounds. As soon as their supply of handkerchiefs was exhausted, she rushed home and tore up her bed sheets to use as bandages. This was her first encounter with war wounds but it wouldn't be her last.

Knowing what was to come, Clara took the initiative by placing advertisements in *The Worcester Spy* newspaper requesting stores, supplies and money for the wounded and needy of the 6th Regiment, stating that she would personally receive and distribute all shipments. The city of Worcester was the first to send assistance, and soon after surrounding towns and cities in Massachusetts followed its example.

The public response was phenomenal. The number of packages sent was so great that Clara's room was filled to the rafters and she was obliged to secure space in a nearby warehouse. In the weeks that followed, as more regiments arrived in Washington, she made it her personal duty to supply them with food, medical provisions and clothing. Due to the lack of any coordinated military organization, the regiments were in desperate need of these supplies. Clara and her associates compensated for this organizational vacuum and worked incredibly hard to establish the shipping and distribution of supplies. She appears to have discovered a serious purpose to her life, a meaning that transcended the desultory offices and schoolrooms that she had previously been associated with.

Throughout the following weeks and months, she began meeting wounded soldiers as they disembarked at the dockside after returning from the swamps of the Chickahominy in the Peninsular Campaign. She personally saw congealed blood and swamp clay thickly encrusted on terrible wounds and men delirious with pain. Clara did what she could to ease their suffering, applying warm water, lotions and clean dressings. She laboured hard, tending men amid the flies and filth, surrounded by festering sores and putrid odours under the sweltering Maryland sun. When one batch was transported off to hospital, another arrived on a seemingly endless production line of human misery. Most women of the day would have probably fainted at these abhorrent sights and smells. Clara instead had discovered her *raison d'etre* and she applied great passion and professionalism to her task.

Reflecting on her service during the civil war in later years she wrote: 'I was strong and thought I might go to the rescue of the men who fell. The first regiment of troops, the old 6th Mass. that fought its way through Baltimore, brought my playmates and neighbours, the partakers of my childhood, the brigades of New Jersey brought scores of my brave boys, the same solid phalanx; and the strongest legions from old Herkimer brought the associates of my seminary days. They formed and crowded around me. What could I do but go with them, or work for them and my country? The patriot blood of my father was warm in my veins. But I struggled long and hard with my sense of propriety, with the appalling fact that I was only a woman whispering in one ear, and thundering in the other the groans of suffering men dying like dogs, unfed and unsheltered, for the life of every institution which had protected and educated me! I said that I struggled with my sense of propriety and I say it with humiliation and shame. I am ashamed that I thought of such a thing.'

Her next intention was to physically go to the battlefields, an aspiration definitely beneath the ladies of polite society at the time. When she requested permission to do this, Union generals were discouraging. It was no place for a woman they would patronizingly assure her, but Clara would not be deterred. The generals' fears were grounded because numerous atrocities were inflicted on civilians living in proximity to the theatre of war by both sides. Property was frequently requisitioned, confiscated without promise of remuneration, and, on occasion, some civilians were executed, beaten or raped for their allegiances, proven or otherwise. Nevertheless, Clara made her way to Manassas in July 1861, where she helped tend to the wounded after Bull Run, the first battle of the civil war. The experience appears to have made her even more determined to get out to other battlefields and this is precisely what she did.

Determined to break with convention and override military red tape, by late spring 1862, following the death of her father, she returned to Washington DC and soon picked up the ropes at her dispensaries and warehouses. She also offered relief to overcrowded transports of wounded and sick men from the Army of the Potomac. She wrote: 'When our armies fought on Cedar Mountain, I broke the shackles and went to the field. Five days and nights with three hours sleep, a narrow escape from capture and some days of getting the wounded into hospitals at Washington brought Saturday, August 30. And if you chance to feel, that the positions I occupied were rough and unseemly for a woman I can only reply that they were rough and unseemly for men. But under all, lay the life of the nation. I had inherited the rich blessing of health and strength of constitution such as are seldom given to woman, and I felt that some return was due from me and that I ought to be there.'

The year 1862 was seminal in the life of Clara Barton. By August she was providing direct battlefield assistance. The reluctant generals had provided her with passes after she had given them her personal assurance that she would neither run nor complain if she was in the line of fire. This 41-year-old spinster must have been aware that she was embarking on a course that entailed great risks to both herself and her associates.

The Union Army was ill-prepared to deal with the wounds contemporary weaponry inflicted on combatants, and the disorganized Medical Corps was poorly provisioned to deal with the problem. Civil war medical procedures such as amputations in proximity to the battlefield were common, and incurred a 27 per cent mortality rate among Union troops. Although surgeons generally used ether or chloroform as an anaesthetic, antiseptic surgery was still in its infancy and many soldiers perished due to infection. Chloroform was first used as an anaesthetic in 1847. Because it allowed surgeons to perform painful operations more slowly, they could better prepare amputation stumps for prostheses. By controlling pain, anaesthesia reduced deaths previously caused by shock. Unfortunately, surgeons were not able to control bleeding and infections until much later. By the time the American Civil War broke out in 1861, both ether and chloroform had been in use for several years as methods of surgical anaesthesia. Chloroform eventually emerged as the more ubiquitously applied anaesthetic because it worked faster than ether and was non-flammable. During the civil war, ether and particularly chloroform became indispensable tools for military doctors, who performed tens of thousands of amputations and other types of procedures for wounded Union and Confederate soldiers.

In 1862 Clara was present at one of the bloodiest and most devastating engagements of the whole American Civil War. The Battle of Antietam was the first invasion of the north by Confederate General Robert E. Lee and the Army of Northern Virginia. After Lee's spectacular victory at the Second Battle of Bull Run during the last two days of August, he chose

Antietam was the bloodiest single day in American military history. The 'Angel on the Battlefield' on this occasion was Ms Clara Barton.

to maintain the offensive in the hope of achieving southern independence by means of a victory on northern soil. Shortly after fording the Potomac River and arriving in Frederick, Lee made the decision to divide his army for the purpose of capturing the Union garrison stationed at Harpers Ferry, while the rest of the Confederates moved north and west toward South Mountain and Hagerstown, Maryland. On 16 September the two armies faced off on opposite ridges near Sharpsburg. Between them lay the foreboding valley of Antietam.

Later on, Clara recalled an incident that would have unnerved even the most steadfast soul:

'The smoke became so dense as to obscure our sight, and the hot sulphurous breath of battle dried our tongues, and parched our lips to bleeding. We were in a slight hollow and all shell, which did not break our guns in front, came directly among or over us, bursting above our heads or burying themselves in the hills beyond. A man lying upon the ground asked for a drink, I stopped to give it, and having raised him with my right hand, was holding him. Just at this moment a bullet sped its free and easy way between us, tearing a hole in my sleeve and found its way into his body. He fell back dead. There was no more to be done for him and I left him to his rest. I have never mended that hole in my sleeve.'

By the end of the battle Clara had contracted a fever of such severity she was unable to walk unaided. However, this didn't prevent her from complaining bitterly to Quartermaster General Rucker that she could have done more if her supplies hadn't been exhausted. Rucker gave his personal assurance that this would never be the case again. Union General Benjamin Butler was so impressed by Clara's tenacity and courage that he officially appointed her as 'Lady in charge' of the hospitals.

Both Union and Confederate armies experienced indescribable suffering at Antietam. After three days of violent combat it produced the single bloodiest day in American history, culminating in the deaths of 12,410 Union and 10,700 Confederate soldiers. Although militarily it ended without a decisive victory for either side, the fact that Lee had retreated back over the river was enough for the Union to proclaim it a success. More importantly, it was a propaganda victory for the Union because the war now obtained a dual purpose. Apart from preserving the union, five days after the Battle of Antietam President Lincoln used it as a catalyst to issue his Emancipation Proclamation, stating that all slaves held in rebelling states were to be freed on 1 January 1863.

During the final year of the war, Clara was informed of the vast number of soldiers missing in action (MIA) that had accumulated throughout the previous four years. She received letters from various parts of the country stating that significant numbers of soldiers had disappeared without a trace. Concerned relatives had no idea what had become of their loved ones, whether they had fallen in battle, were suffering in Confederate POW camps, or had perished in some other way. On the strength of this, in the spring of 1865 Clara took it upon herself to personally assist in discovering the fates of some of these men. She began by distributing printed lists of MIAs to be displayed in conspicuous places requesting information from anyone able to help. Using her skill as an administrator she initiated and organized a government-supported department that dealt with up to 100 letters a day. On the basis of this she made a nationwide appeal for information that produced significant results. Clara and her assistants received and answered more than 63,000 letters and identified over 22,000 missing men.

One Union soldier named Dorrence Atwater had been a POW at the notorious Confederate prison at Andersonville. He secretly made an official list of the dead and their burial, hiding a list of more than 13,000 names in his coat lining. Up to 45,000 Union soldiers suffered unimaginable horrors while being held at Andersonville. During the worst months, 100 men died each day from malnutrition, exposure and communicable disease. After the war, Andersonville commandant Captain Henry Wirz was arrested and found guilty by a military tribunal. He was hanged in Washington DC on 10 November 1865. He was the only person executed for war crimes during the American Civil War.

CHAPTER EIGHT

THE GIRL WHO SAW TOO MUCH

Everyone save the terminally unenlightened knows that the Battle of Gettysburg in the American Civil War was a cataclysmic clash of giants, of contesting ideologies that dealt out death in a gargantuan three-day struggle to claim the field. It was a battle that would ultimately help to decide the uncertain future of a young nation.

Some say that Gettysburg was America's Waterloo and there are indeed similarities. But this chapter will not focus on the tactics and the strategy of the battle, or the mindsets of the key participants. Instead it will recount the devastating experiences of one young angel who was inadvertently swept up in the sequence of events and was confronted with the grim reality of battle and its casualties.

Her name was Matilda Jane Pierce, but everybody called her Tillie. She was the youngest of four children, born on 11 March 1848 in a house that can still be seen today on the corner of Baltimore and Breckenridge Streets in Gettysburg. Her father and mother were James and Margaret, and she had a younger brother, Franklin, and two older brothers, James Shaw and William H., both of whom were training to become butchers like their father. They would have been a relatively wealthy family thanks to their father's thriving business.

Tillie was very much the demure, modest young lady typical of mid-nineteenth-century America. Long before reaching maturity her mother would have taught her the necessary domestic skills of cooking, sewing, cleaning and how to entertain guests. Before the winds of war came to Gettysburg in 1863 and blew everything away Tillie and her family would have led peaceful, uneventful lives.

Three weeks before the epic battle rumours began circulating in Gettysburg that Confederate troops were heading in their direction. The town was in a strategically important position, at the crossroads of several routes between Shippensburg and Baltimore, and Philadelphia and Pittsburgh. Then, the rumours became reality in mid-June when General Robert E. Lee's Confederate Army crossed into Pennsylvania. By 29 June they had reached the Susquehanna River opposite Harrisburg at Wrightsville, just a few miles from Gettysburg.

One Friday afternoon while Tillie was attending a literary exercises class at the respectable Eyster School for Young Ladies she heard someone excitedly shouting, 'the rebels are coming'. The anxiety this unwelcome news provoked among the young girls was almost palpable. Within

moments the class teacher, Ms Eyster, a veritable island of calm, was giving instructions to her pupils to run home to their families as fast as they could. No further inducement was required as the girls funnelled to the exit with all the grace of stampeding longhorns.

Tillie and some other girls had briefly gazed out toward the Theological Seminary building nearby and saw what appeared to be an ominous-looking dense mass in the far distance moving in their direction.

Tillie just managed to reach her own front door before seeing a number of mounted Confederate soldiers entering the street where she lived. The mounted raiders were followed by infantry, who

Fifteen-year-old Tillie Pierce tended scores of wounded soldiers at the

began scavenging in earnest and ransacking homes looking for any food or plunder they could lay their hands on. Some other citizens must have been better informed than young Tillie about the impending arrival of these Johnny Rebs because most merchants and bankers had already moved their valuables to places of safety, and most Gettysburg citizens had sent their horses as far away as possible to the cemetery at Baltimore Pike. Tillie later described the shock she felt as she watched soldiers ravage her family's food stores like men possessed. These Confederate 'raiders' also requisitioned a horse from the Pierce family before they left.

Much to the relief of the people of Gettysburg, by noon on Tuesday, 30 June, Union cavalry began arriving on the outskirts of town. They entered from the north along Washington Street, turned west on Chamberlain Street and rode past the Theological Seminary building in significant numbers. The seminary would provide a good vantage point to establish a lookout post the following day for the commander of the 1st Division Cavalry Corps, Brigadier General John Buford. When Buford's cavalry recognized General James Pettigrew's brigade of infantry advancing along the Chambersburg Pike toward Gettysburg, the objective for the first day of battle to commence the following afternoon had been achieved. The Union Army had found the enemy force, or at least a part of it.

Oblivious to the machinations of generals and officers, the Pierce family rose early the following day. The family gathered outside on the street to wave, cheer and watch a seemingly endless train of cavalry, infantry and loaded supply wagons passing through the town. It was almost noon before the last wagon had passed when Tillie went to see her next-door neighbour Mrs Shriver, whose husband was serving with the Union Army. Mrs Shriver said that she didn't feel safe remaining in her home and that she was going to leave town and visit her father, Jacob Weikert, who owned a small farmstead south of the town, on the Taneytown road at the eastern slope of a well-known promontory called Little Round Top. Mrs Shriver had two young children to care for and asked Tillie to join them, with the assurance that she would also be safer away from the fighting. Tillie's parents gladly gave their consent. The sound of cannon and rifle would have been clearly audible at the Pierce household as Tillie packed a small case with some meagre belongings and set off with Mrs Shriver and her children.

It's a well-documented fact that neither Confederate commander General Lee nor General George Gordon Meade, commander of the Union Army of the Potomac, had expected to engage at Gettysburg. Pure coincidence had drawn these two forces together and that first day's battle resulted in a definite but indecisive victory for the Confederates. They arrived with numerical superiority from the west and the north and drove the Union forces back through town in disarray.

To proceed to the Weikert farm by means of the Taneytown road was a potentially precarious decision, because this highway was vulnerable to a Confederate attack. At one particular juncture during the battle Major General Daniel Sickles took the decision to abandon his position on the southern stretch of Cemetery Ridge, completely exposing the Taneytown Road, which was at the time an essential line of communication for General Meade's Union forces. A determined push by the Confederate Army would have been able to sever what was part of the essential Union supply line just behind the ridge. More importantly, Tillie, Mrs Shriver and the children could have been blown to pieces. Tillie later wrote:

'About 1 o'clock we started out on foot; the battle still going on ... As we were passing along the Cemetery hill our men were already planting cannon. They told us to hurry as fast as possible that we were in great danger of being shot by Rebels, whom they expected would shell toward us at any moment. We fairly ran to get out of this new danger. As I looked toward the Seminary Ridge I could see and hear the confusion of the battle. Troops moving hither and thither; the smoke of the conflict arising from the fields; shells bursting in the air together with the din, rising and falling, in mighty undulations. These things, beheld for the first time, filled my soul with the greatest apprehensions. We soon reached the Taneytown road, and while traveling along, were overtaken by an ambulance wagon in which was the body of a dead soldier. Some of them told us that it was the body of General Reynolds, and that he had been killed during the forenoon in the battle.'

On the way they passed the Leister farm, which is also still there at the intersection with Hunt Avenue. It's a modest two-storey house with a whitewashed picket fence that was destined to become the Union commander's headquarters for the duration of the battle. As the small group approached the house they were accosted by a friendly Union soldier who said that he was going to ask someone to accompany them to their destination, on the premise that it was very dangerous to remain at their present location. They entered the Leister farm and before long the soldier returned and told them that there was a wagon approaching, and that he would attempt to secure a lift for them. Grateful for this display of kindness, Tillie, Mrs Shriver and her children were bundled aboard an already full wagon. It was an arduous journey because the road was now so well worn that mud almost reached the axles.

The little group was welcomed with open arms when they safely arrived at the farm but they were by no means out of danger. While they were settling in their attention was drawn to the sound of Union artillery passing by and being spurred on with great urgency. As Tillie watched she shuddered as one of the loaded caissons exploded, catapulting a soldier into the air. Other soldiers quickly carried the poor man's limp body into the farmhouse. Observing her first sight of someone badly wounded, Tillie noticed that his eyes had been blown out and he was scorched black from head to toe. Despite the severity of his condition the soldier still managed to feebly utter, 'Oh dear I forgot to read my Bible today, what will my poor wife and children say?'

After the artillerymen had passed, columns of infantry approached. Tillie's first task was to provide water from a nearby well for these troops who appeared to her young eyes to be very tired and thirsty. She would have had little or no idea of the sheer complexity or grim reality of nineteenth-century warfare, but she would soon learn what it entailed when she saw the effects of musket balls and conical bullets fired from .58 calibre rifles that ripped through flesh and pulverized bones, while iron cannonballs dismembered infantry and tore through limbs.

As the afternoon drew to a close, wounded men began arriving at the Weikert farm. Many imparted horror stories about how they had witnessed terrible scenes of death and destruction during the fighting on that first day. As the conflict intensified the initial trickle of wounded men soon swelled to a deluge. Some were walking wounded while others were ferried in on makeshift ambulances. Before nightfall had set in the Weikert house and adjacent barn was brimming to the rafters. Tillie wrote:

'That evening Beckie Weikert, the daughter at home, and I went out to the barn to see what was transpiring there. Nothing before in my experience had ever paralleled the sight we then and there beheld. There were the groaning and crying, the struggling and dying, crowded side by side, while attendants sought to aid and relieve them as best they could. We were so overcome by the sad and awful spectacle that we hastened back to the house weeping bitterly.'

But things did not improve there. She continued:

'As we entered the basement or cellar-kitchen of the house, we found many nurses making beef tea for the wounded. Seeing that we were crying they inquired as to the cause. We told them where we had been and what we had seen. They no doubt appreciated our feelings for they at once endeavoured to cheer us by telling funny stories, and ridiculing our tears ... I remember that at this time a chaplain, who was present in the kitchen, stepped up to me while I was attending to some duty and said, "Little girl, do all you can for the poor soldiers and the Lord will reward you." I looked up in his face and laughed, but at once felt ashamed of my conduct and begged his pardon. After telling him what Beckie and I had seen, how the nurses had derided us for crying and that I now laughed when I should not, being unable to help myself, he remarked, "Well it is much better for you and the soldiers to be in a cheerful mood." The first day had passed, and with the rest of the family, I retired, surrounded with strange and appalling events, and many new visions passing rapidly through my mind.'

Attempting to comprehend the sights, smells and sounds that confronted Tillie during her first encounter with the wounded and dying is almost inconceivable. The assault on her senses would have shocked and outraged her, but where other young ladies would have become catatonic with fear she appears to have risen to the challenge. Maybe this could be attributed to being raised in the household of a butcher. She would have been no stranger to blood and guts and this probably stood her in good stead to deal with the results of the butchery she witnessed in that farmhouse at Gettysburg.

The following day, as reinforcements from both sides arrived the fighting escalated and intensified. General Robert E. Lee had formulated a plan for his Confederates to attack both flanks of the Union line on Cemetery Ridge. He launched a withering attack against the Union positions on the heights, and also Little Round Top further south, but despite repeated attempts he failed to remove the defenders. He had issued his orders based on errant intelligence that claimed the Round Tops and the southern end of Cemetery Ridge were unoccupied by Union troops. The result was three hours of total carnage that gained nothing of any tactical value for his Army of Northern Virginia apart from increasing the casualties on both sides.

The new day dawned 2 July with cobalt clear blue skies and some low-lying morning mist in the valleys on a landscape that would soon erupt to rebel yells and flying lead. By mid-morning there was frenzied activity outside the Weikert farm on the Taneytown road as this vital supply artery of the Union forces resounded to the clamour of ammunition and artillery trains coursing through the muddy road on their way to the battlefield. Outside, the farm boxes containing corpses began to accumulate while inside the wounded suffered agonizing discomfort from the pain of their wounds and the rising heat. The putrid smell of human effluence and dismembered limbs decomposing in the humid Pennsylvania heat alone would have been noticeable from at least 50 yards.

Meanwhile, Mrs Weikert and her daughters worked incredibly hard, baking bread for the wounded men and turning the farmhouse kitchen into a food production line. Just before noon the farmhouse foundation shook to the thunderous roar of cannonades emanating from the direction of the Round Tops. In the back garden, lifeless bodies of soldiers who had been picked off by Confederate snipers lay around in grotesque ballet poses, steaming and bleeding out in the unremitting heat of the midday sun. As the deafening cannonades increased in ferocity one union soldier suggested to the Weikert family that they should retire to a safer location. The family willingly acquiesced – only to be told when they arrived at their new safe place to return to the Weikert farm, as it was deemed to be safer. They were not best pleased.

Back at the Weikert farm and a little bewildered, they all returned to their tasks. Sometime during the late afternoon soldiers caused considerable consternation when they began shouting that rebels were approaching the farmhouse rapidly. After registering this moment, Tillie displayed the characteristic inquisitiveness of a 15-year-old and went to see for herself. Grabbing a pair of field glasses from an unconscious officer, she peered tenuously across the fields at the south side of the farm where she indeed saw Confederate soldiers approaching through the fields. At that time she had a brother in the 1st Regiment Pennsylvania Reserves that had been hurriedly dispatched to counteract this potential threat to the Union supply lines. Within moments the two opposing forces had squared off against each other and were unleashing their first volleys of lead. The exchange was brief but intense, culminating in the Confederate troops retreating hastily towards the Round Tops.

The situation abated for now but more wounded were arriving at the Weikert Farm. Tillie sat with one of them and wrote about the conversation they shared: 'I then took the candle and sat down beside the wounded man. I talked to him and asked if he was injured badly. He answered "Yes, pretty badly." I then asked him if he suffered much, to which he replied "Yes, I do now, but I hope in the morning I will be better." I told him if there was anything I could do for him I would be so glad to do it, if he would only tell me what. The poor man looked so earnestly into my face, saying, "Will you promise me to come back in the morning to see me?" I replied "Yes, indeed." And he seemed so satisfied, and faintly smiled.'

The soldier was General Stephen H. Weed. He died during the night from wounds sustained during the height of the fighting at Little Round Top. His vanguard successfully repelled a Confederate attack but Weed was mortally wounded in the chest, probably by a Confederate sniper firing from the direction of Devil's Den. According to a witness his last words were allegedly, 'I would rather die here than that the rebels should gain an inch of this ground.' But according to Tillie those words were most definitely not his last.

The next day dawned with the same ominous hallmarks as the previous one: more wounded arriving, more cannonballs roaring overhead and even more misery and death to contend with. Some of the projectiles were now landing in dangerously close proximity to the small farmhouse. The situation deteriorated to such an extent that a decision was taken to evacuate the Weikert family, Mrs Shriver's family and Tillie for a second time to a safer location near the Baltimore Pike. As they were leaving they saw the Union 6th Corps reserve command arriving. Soon Tillie and the others reached the Taneytown Road and Baltimore Pike, where she saw some rebel prisoners. They met some other families at a farmhouse there who were also sheltering from the fighting, but by evening the sounds of battle had begun to dissipate. Tillie and the rest returned to the Weikert farm before the sun had dissolved beneath a blood red sky. When they arrived at the farm they were confronted with a hellish tableau.

She later wrote: 'Amputating benches had been placed about the house. I must have become inured to seeing the terrors of battle, else I could hardly have gazed upon the scenes now presented. I was looking out of one of the windows facing the front yard. Near the basement door, and directly underneath the window I was at, stood one of these benches. I saw them lifting the poor men upon it, then the surgeons sawing and cutting off arms and legs, then again probing and picking bullets from the flesh … To the south of the house and just outside of the yard, I noticed a pile of limbs higher than the fence.'

Every approach path was congested with wounded and dying men and inside the farm it was even worse. Tillie described seeing every room packed tight with casualties in all stages of suffering. The floors would have been steeped inches deep with congealed blood and the air would have been rendered foul with putrid odours. All accompanied by a deathly, resonant chorus of tormented moans, cries and screams of pain.

Tillie would eventually be reunited with her family, who miraculously all survived the ordeal unscathed. Tillie hadn't had much sleep the past few days, which made her understandably cranky. She had walked the battlefield, seen the carnage and witnessed some terrible things. She would carry the memory of that battle in her heart for the rest of her natural life. Her diary is a heart-rending testament to courage, tenacity and suffering that echoes to this day.

CHAPTER NINE

HENRY AND THE RED CROSS

No book about battlefield nurses and doctors would be complete without space devoted to Henry Dunant – the wonderful, often conflicted founder of the Red Cross. In his lifetime, Dunant would be both revered and demonized by society. He was that rare combination of businessman and philanthropist who extolled utopian ideas to a world that wasn't always receptive.

The Red Cross was created as a direct response to Dunant's experiences immediately after the bloody Battle of Solferino on 24 June 1859. The battle was the final encounter in the Second Italian War of Independence. France and the Kingdom of Piedmont-Sardinia fought against the Austrian Empire, which at the time controlled a significant piece of northern Italy. It was the last major battle in world history where all the armies were personally commanded by their respective monarchs. Perhaps that was why the conflict degenerated into such a disastrous free-for-all. Thanks to poor reconnaissance and questionable military acumen, the opposing armies became embroiled in a horrendous 15-hour slogging match in a field just south of Lake Garda, in Italy. While the French-Italian army was victorious it came at a terrible cost, with appallingly high casualties on both sides.

Henry Dunant was born in Geneva on 8 May 1828 and hailed from a fairly affluent, devoutly Calvinist family. His father, Jean-Jacques Dunant, was the superintendent of an orphanage and supervisor of prisons. His mother, Antoinette Dunant-Colladon, was a social activist. Thus Henry Dunant was exposed to philanthropic ideologies from a very early age.

At 21, having failed to demonstrate any serious academic prowess Dunant dropped out of college and accepted an apprenticeship at Lullin et Sautter, a banking firm. On 30 November 1852 he founded the Geneva branch of the YMCA, exchanging letters with like-minded organizations in England, France, Germany, Holland and the US. In 1855, while attending a meeting in Paris with some friends, he made further connections with the YMCA, which had been founded in London in 1844 by George Williams. Dunant suggested that all these Christian-based groups should cooperate internationally, which resulted in the formation of the World Alliance of YMCAs.

Determined to find his place in the world, in 1853 Dunant accepted a commission to travel to Algeria to take charge of the Swiss colony of Sétif. Three years later, after being granted land in French-occupied Algeria, he started a corn growing and trading company there, the Financial and Industrial Company of Mons-Djémila Mills. Wanting to develop a healthy, altruistic attitude to those he employed, Dunant insisted that his Algerian workers were both well paid and well provisioned. Furthermore, to gain a better understanding of the indigenous people he studied Islam, took Arabic lessons and practised Arabic calligraphy. In the process he developed a lifelong affection for North Africans.

The only serious problem he encountered was in dealing with the French authorities. He needed their cooperation to legally acquire land for his business so that he could grow wheat and put his plans into action. The location had been judiciously chosen, he had sufficient capital and the mill itself was fitted with the most modern equipment. The pieces were in place for a potentially successful business, but he had underestimated the bloody-mindedness of the French bureaucrats who went to great lengths to frustrate and disregard Dunant's requests. In desperation, he went to Paris and spent many fruitless hours waiting patiently outside the offices of various ministers. He got a lot of promises but, not surprisingly, little support. It was time to pull out all the stops.

The founder of the Red Cross, Mr Henry Dunant, was devastated by the duplicitous machinations of his Swiss colleagues. He never forgave them.

He wrote a rather flattering biography about Emperor Napoleon III and proposed presenting it to the man himself. This would also give him the opportunity to go over the heads of the emperor's recalcitrant ministers and ask Napoleon III to grant him the land rights he needed. After going through the necessary channels he discovered that the emperor was indisposed, off fighting a war in Lombardy.

Undeterred, Dunant made his way to Italy. However, he was not prepared for the terrible sights that greeted him when he reached Napoleon III's headquarters in the small town of Solferino. The whole region had been devastated by an engagement that produced the bloodiest carnage Europe had experienced since the epic Battle of Waterloo.

Dunant had seen the tragic aftermath of the 1859 Battle of Solferino first-hand, when he toured the battlefield the day after the engagement. Solferino was a particularly bloody encounter where 40,000 men were killed or wounded in just 15 intense, ferocious hours of fighting. Readers were shocked by Dunant's book when it was published in 1862, especially its vivid and graphic descriptions of the violence and brutality of armed conflict. They were equally moved by his account of the plight of the wounded and of the noble but pitifully inadequate efforts that he and his little band of helpers had made to alleviate their suffering. His proposals for ameliorating the condition of the wounded in future wars so impressed the European public and many well-placed supporters that he had no problem raising volunteers and gaining support for his organization, which became the Red Cross.

On 9 July 1859 he wrote a heart-rending piece which appeared in the *Journal de Geneve*. It read:

'For 3 days I have been treating the wounded from Solferino at Castiglione and have cared for more than one thousand men in misery. We have had 40,000 wounded, of which as many allies as Austrians, involved in this terrible affair. There are not sufficient doctors, and I had to replace them as well as I could with the help of some local women and some prisoners who were in a fit condition. At the moment of the armies' encounter, I immediately proceeded from Brescia to the battlefield; nothing can describe the grievous

The terrible Battle of Solferino provided all the impetus Dunant needed to establish the Red Cross.

consequence of this battle; to find anything in keeping with it, one has to revert to the most famous battles of the First Empire. The Crimean war was nothing in comparison.

'Forgive me for writing to you in the middle of a battlefield where there is no sense of measure in one's expressions. But the battlefield itself is nothing even with its heaps of dead bodies, and dying men, in comparison to the church where 500 wounded are piled up. For three days, every quarter of an hour, I see a man's soul departing from this world in the midst of unforgettable suffering.'

Dunant never got his audience with Napoleon III. He was far too busy helping the casualties on the battlefield. A few years later he wrote about his experiences in the book, *A Memory of Solferino*. Its sole purpose was to raise public awareness about the horrors of war. He promoted the book throughout Europe, gathering support for his plans to establish an independent aid organization. He started a group known as the Committee of Five, which later became the International Committee of the Red Cross, formed in Geneva in 1863. It fulfilled Dunant's desire for the creation of a civilian relief corps to respond to human suffering during conflict, and for establishing rules regarding the conduct of war. Some months later, diplomats from 16 nations, assisted by this committee, along with representatives of military, humanitarian and medical services, negotiated and signed up to a treaty that comprised ten articles. The treaty was signed on 22 August 1864, and became known in English as the Geneva Convention. He later claimed that the works of three writers, all of them women, influenced him greatly. They were Harriet Beecher Stowe, Florence Nightingale and Elizabeth Fry.

It was agreed by the Convention that during times of conflict the Red Cross would be guaranteed neutrality for its ambulances, hospitals and medical workers and their equipment. The same applied for local inhabitants who were helping the wounded. It also provided for wounded enemy soldiers and stipulated that their captors had an obligation to treat their wounds or to arrange for this to be done. It spelled out the obligation of armies to search for and collect the wounded. The inverse Swiss flag was identified as the international symbol of the organization. By the end of 1867, 21 nations had signed up to the Geneva Convention.

However, 1867 turned out to be a disastrous year for Dunant. While focusing on the Red Cross and the Geneva Convention he had seriously neglected his business interests. The Credit Genevois bank, on whose board of directors he sat, went bankrupt. Along with his fellow directors, Dunant was convicted of deception. This left him saddled with debts of almost 5 million francs. At only 39 years of age, and just eight years after the Battle of Solferino, Dunant had lost everything – even his position in the growing Red Cross movement.

Reduced to living in abject poverty, Dunant wandered around Europe until 1887, when, blighted by illness, he returned to Switzerland and settled in the mountain village of Heiden, a shadow of his former self. He would have remained living in total obscurity if it hadn't been for Georg Baumberger, the chief editor of the St Gall newspaper *Die Ostschweiz (The*

East Swiss). He had been hiking in the mountains near Heiden when he heard about a hospitalized old man claiming to be the founder of the Red Cross. Intrigued, the journalist made an appointment to interview Dunant. The result was the article 'Henri Dunant, the founder of the Red Cross', which appeared in the German illustrated magazine *Über Land und Meer* (*Over Land and Lake*) and which was widely reprinted throughout Europe. This was followed by an 1897 book about the origins of the Red Cross which wrote Dunant's name back into the story. Henri Dunant began to receive honours and accolades from all quarters, not the least of which was the award of the very first Nobel Peace Prize in 1901, which he shared with the French peace activist Frederic Passy.

The Nobel Peace Prize helped to alleviate Dunant's feelings of societal rejection and humiliation, but he didn't spend any of the considerable prize money on himself. He left the money to the people who had cared for him in Heiden, and funded a free hospital room for the poor there. He also made substantial donations to various charities in Norway and Switzerland. Henry Dunant died peacefully on 30 October 1910.

While Dunant was busy forming the Red Cross in Europe, Clara Barton was laying the foundations for the institution in the United States. She had had an accomplished medical career during the American Civil War (see pages 106–13). In the autumn of 1869 Clara Barton took her doctor's advice and travelled to Europe for three years' rest. While visiting Geneva she heard about Henry Dunant's book, *A Memory of Solferino*, which had inspired the establishment of the Geneva Convention and the Red Cross.

On 19 July 1870, four days after the outbreak of the Franco-Prussian War, officials from the International Red Cross of Europe approached Barton, who at that time was still recuperating in Switzerland. The committee told Clara they had heard of her and were deeply impressed by her work during the American Civil War. At first, she declined their invitation to visit the frontlines, citing health reasons. Eventually, though, her curiosity got the better of her. Based on what she saw, Clara decided to establish the Red Cross in America. She wrote: 'As I journeyed on and saw the work of these Red Cross societies in the field, accomplishing in four months under their systematic organization what we failed to accomplish in four years

Clara Barton served her country with great distinction during the Civil War and went on to establish the Red Cross in America.

without it. No mistakes, no needless suffering, no starving, no lack of care, no waste, no confusion, but order, plenty, cleanliness and comfort wherever that little flag made its way, a whole continent marshalled under the banner of the Red Cross, as I saw all this, and joined and worked in it, you will not wonder that I said to myself "if I live to return to my country I will try to make my people understand the Red Cross and that treaty." But I did more than resolve, I promised other nations I would do it, and other reasons pressed me to remember my promise.'

In 1877, Clara lobbied President Rutherford B. Hayes in an attempt to procure his endorsement of the Geneva Convention. Hayes expressed interest at first but had serious reservations regarding the treaty's connotations that he regarded as a 'possible entangling alliance' with European nations. This prompted him to ultimately reject her petition. Impervious to this rejection, Clara established the American Red Cross and held the first meeting in her Washington apartment on 21 May 1881. Later that year she approached President James Garfield about ratifying the Geneva treaty. He appeared to be supportive, but his death from an assassin's bullet in September 1881 put paid to that. His successor, Chester A. Arthur, did agree to sign the treaty and, on 16 May 1882, the US Senate ratified it. The US Congress awarded the American Red Cross its first federal charter in 1900 and again in 1905, the year after 83-year-old Clara resigned as president of the organization.

Like Florence Nightingale, Clara Barton could be pertinacious and rarely listened to advice or suggestions from other members of her group. But it's indisputable that she embodies the quintessential frontline nurse, someone who actively endeavoured to be accepted in a field that, until that point, had been an exclusively male domain. The American Civil War provided her with a sense of purpose, and despite suffering a number of nervous breakdowns she extolled an enduring, seemingly irrepressible confidence and firm belief in her convictions. She disdained personal criticism, had the capacity on occasion to exaggerate her achievements and stoically believed in her self-projected image.

There were times when she vacillated between self-righteousness and blatant intransigence, but her contribution to the welfare and care of wounded soldiers is completely unassailable. Clara Barton was a trailblazer and displayed incredible courage and fortitude. It's for these and many other qualities that this battlefield angel deserves to be remembered. She died at her home in Glen Echo, Maryland, in 1912 at the grand old age of 91.

After the establishment of the Red Cross by these pioneers, the institution went on to play a major role in combat medicine in both world wars and throughout the twentieth century. On 21 August 1914, the International Committee of the Red Cross (ICRC) established the International Prisoners-of-War Agency in Geneva. All nations caught up in World War I signed up to the agreement and submitted lists of prisoners. The Agency received 400,000 pages of documents: lists of prisoners' names and records of capture, transfers between camps and deaths in detention. The ICRC organized vital lines of communication in an effort to restore contact between relatives separated by war, and this factor still remains a vital part of the work the organization does today.

In World War II, the Red Cross sent official delegates on missions to inspect 524 prisoner-of-war and internment camps in Europe, the French colonies in North Africa, India and Japan. They interviewed both prisoners and camp authorities, inspected conditions in the camps, checked hygiene, food and working conditions, sometimes to no avail. They also checked whether prisoners were being treated humanely and were able to write to their families in accordance with the Geneva Convention. They also supplied Red Cross packages (which did not always reach their intended recipients, as German guards were known to steal them). In December 1944, the American Red Cross provided Christmas packages to POWs in Germany. Over 75,000 units were shipped from Philadelphia to Gothenburg, before being transported by neutral Swedish vessels to northern Germany.

After World War II, the Red Cross was rightfully criticized for not providing assistance for Jews transported to concentration camps. In their defence they said that Jews were not officially considered to be prisoners of war and, lacking a specific legal basis, the organization was bound by its traditional procedures and hindered in its ability to act by its ties with the Swiss establishment. In short, the Red Cross didn't have the authority to intervene. Its lack of action on behalf of victims of the Holocaust and other persecuted groups is a stain on an otherwise unblemished reputation.

Since its inception the work of an ICRC delegate had always been a male preserve. In January 1949, an amendment in the regulation on the status of ICRC delegates stipulated that 'only Swiss citizens of both sexes and good reputation may be taken into consideration as members of delegations'. Jeanne Egger became the first ICRC delegate in 1962, though it was not until the 1970s that women more commonly achieved this position.

PART TWO

HEALING HEARTS AND MINDS

CHAPTER TEN

THE REAL EDITH CAVELL

History records Edith Cavell was a British nurse and humanitarian. So much has been written about her throughout the decades it has become difficult to separate the woman from the legend. The intrinsic propaganda value of her death to British authorities during World War I was incalculable. Since 1915, disseminated by books, articles and films, the legend of this courageous nurse has continued to grow. Few war heroes have received as many posthumous tributes as Nurse Edith Cavell, and there were few incidents during World War I that provoked as much indignation and outrage as the execution of this seemingly innocuous nurse. She has been described as a martyr, a saint and a legendary figure who was cruelly executed by the Germans. It's all very black and white, maybe too clean cut. She was grace and kindness incarnate and the Germans were evil and depraved, end of story. But was it all that straightforward?

In the wee small hours of 12 October 1915, long before the first light of dawn permeated the overcast sky, two cars trundled over uneven cobbled streets towards the Brussels suburb of Schaerbeek. One of them was transporting a British woman to her place of execution. On 4 August 1915, a year after Britain had declared war on Germany, Edith Cavell was arrested in Brussels, accused and found guilty by a German military tribunal of having played an active role in helping Allied soldiers to escape occupied Belgium. Being a painfully honest person, she never denied the charges and was held in solitary confinement in St Gilles prison in Brussels until she attended a trial that lasted just two days, the outcome of which was a sentence of death by firing squad.

The British government has always vigorously refuted German claims that Cavell was a spy. However, according to one former director-general of MI5, apart from assisting Allied soldiers escape occupied Belgium, the British nurse really did help to smuggle out intelligence. Recent discoveries in Belgian archives revealed strong evidence that clearly incriminates Cavell as part of a clandestine network. One young Belgian mining engineer, who smuggled British soldiers to Cavell's organization in 1914, was sentenced to 15 years' hard labour for his activities. In his letters he graphically described how he provided the organization with intelligence on German military operations, information about German trench systems, ammunition dumps and the whereabouts of enemy aircraft.

Edith Cavell was allegedly aware of this information and passed it on through secret channels to the British intelligence services. So, it's entirely possible that she wasn't as innocent as the British press claimed. On the other hand, it's difficult to ascertain precisely how proactive she was within the underground organization. She knew how to relay secret messages, and it's been conclusively proven that key members of her network were in contact with the Secret Service Bureau, the precursor to MI6, and other Allied intelligence agencies. General Moritz Von Bissing, the German military governor of Belgium who signed the warrant for Cavell's execution, maintained that far from being the innocent victim of circumstance she gave her full compliance to the espionage operation.

Throughout World War I German occupation authorities in Belgium arrested hundreds of women for participating in espionage. These activities were described as treason and, depending on the severity of the charge, were punishable by forced labour or execution. Of the ten women who were arrested in Belgium and northern France between 1914 and 1918, six were Belgian, three were French and one was British.

Edith Louisa Cavell was born into a devoutly religious family in Swardeston, Norfolk, on 4 December 1865. Her parents were Reverend

Despite American diplomatic intervention, the Germans executed Edith Cavell during World War I. She knew the risks and was guilty as charged.

Frederick Cavell, an Anglican vicar, and Louisa Sophia Cavell. Faith played an important role in Edith's life and she and her family were all active in local charities. Edith even donated money to a hospital in Bavaria for the purchase of medical equipment, and for her generosity she became known as the 'English Angel'.

Having learned to speak French fluently at boarding school, she took a post as governess to the François family in Brussels. This was the start of Edith Cavell's enduring love affair with Belgium and the Belgian people. An early example of Edith's unimpeachable honesty was revealed when Madame François asked her to tell some unexpected visitors that she was not at home and Edith refused.

In April 1895 she decided to become a nurse and was accepted into a training programme for at the Fountains Fever Hospital in Lower Tooting, London. She graduated in September the following year and remained at the hospital, where she was eventually promoted to staff nurse.

In 1907, Dr Antoine Depage, a Belgian physician and hospital director, persuaded Cavell to accept a position as matron at a recently opened nursing school, the *L'École Belge d'Infirmières Diplômées* in Brussels. At a time when most Belgian hospitals were staffed by nuns, nurses who were not part of the religious establishment were unjustly vilified as women of dubious reputation. Dr Depage wanted to move the institute away from traditional religion-based care and make it a more secular, science-orientated organization. During her brief career in Belgium, Edith succeeded in modernizing the standard of Belgian nursing and gained wide recognition for her work. She helped train many nurses who went on to staff other hospitals, nursing homes and schools around the country, including the clinic at the forbidding St Gilles prison, a place she would get to know better later on. Edith Cavell had found her place in the world and was delighted at the opportunity to teach her chosen profession to young Belgian student nurses. She wrote: 'One of our first duties was to recruit the nurses. The old idea that it is a disgrace for women to work is still held in Belgium, and women of good birth and education still think they lose caste by earning their own living ... These Belgian probationers have goodwill, courage, and perseverance, and in three years' time they will look back on the first days of trial with wonder. The spread of light and knowledge is bound to follow in years to come. The nurses will not only teach, as none others have the opportunity of doing, the laws of health and the prevention and healing of disease, they will show their countrywomen that education and position do not constitute a bar to an independent life, they are rather a good and solid foundation on which to build a career which demands the best and highest qualities that womanhood can offer.'

In 1909 she visited England as a delegate to the International Council of Nurses held in London. Her description of the work she was attempting to conduct in Brussels made a deep and lasting impression on the other delegates.

When war broke out in 1914 Cavell was in England visiting her family, and despite their vehement protests they failed to dissuade her from returning to Belgium. 'My duty is with my nurses,' she wrote to a friend.

On 4 August 1914 the German Army ignored Belgium's neutrality and invaded the country, just days after Cavell's return to Brussels. It was the culmination of the domino effect that had started with the assassination of Archduke Franz Ferdinand in Sarajevo. Britain had guaranteed Belgium's neutrality and was consequently obliged to declare war on Germany for this infraction. Edith Cavell joined the Red Cross, and the Berkendael Institute where she worked was converted into a Red Cross hospital for wounded soldiers of all nations. Even though Cavell was a citizen of an enemy nation, German military authorities displayed remarkable tolerance by allowing her to continue her work as a Red Cross nurse.

Around this time she wrote extensively for a few British newspapers and expressed her horror at the suffering she was witnessing in Brussels. As a Red Cross nurse, although she was critical of some of the actions of the German invaders, she managed to retain an outwardly neutral stance and was careful not to use inflammatory language in her descriptions. Writing in *The Nursing Mirror and Midwives Journal* in April 1915, Cavell described the situation in Belgium under German occupation:

'From the day of the occupation till now we have been cut off from the world outside. Newspapers were first censored, then suppressed, and are now printed under German auspices; all coming from abroad were for a time forbidden, and now none are allowed from England. The telephone service was taken over by the enemy, and we were shortly deprived of its use. The post, too, was stopped, and, though now resumed to certain towns and countries, all letters must be left open and contain no news of the war or of anything of importance. The few trains that run for passengers are in German hands, and wherever you go you must have, and pay for, a passport … No one speaks to his neighbour in the tram, for he may be a spy.'

Belgium had little to thank the German invaders for. While most historians rightfully focus on the numerous atrocities committed by German forces in World War II, not much attention is paid to the terrible acts of violence and destruction they perpetrated against the Belgian people in World War I, which can be regarded as a grim precursor. Many outside the country considered these acts as pure, undiluted Allied propaganda, but the truth was far more sinister. As the German juggernaut marched through neutral Belgium in 1914 it reduced once beautiful cities such as Leuven to rubble. They completely destroyed the world-famous library there that housed priceless, centuries-old manuscripts. Then they conducted reprisals against the civilian population, summarily executing hundreds. Within two months of the occupation it is estimated that the Germans murdered around 5,500 Belgian citizens.

On 15 August 1914, two German battalions entered the town of Dinant. French soldiers successfully repulsed the first attack within a few hours. During this encounter, a young French lieutenant by the name of Charles de Gaulle was wounded. Outraged at the show of defiance by the French Army, the Germans made a second successful attempt to subjugate the town. In retribution against the citizens of Dinant they executed 674 civilians, roughly 10 per cent of the population. Among them were 26 pensioners, 76 women and 37 children. Félix Fivet, a three-week-old baby, was impaled on a German bayonet. More than 1,100 houses were completely destroyed, including the town hall and a museum. Eighty per cent of the town was destroyed and it was the largest massacre the Germans inflicted on the civilian population during that reign of terror in 1914. Those early British recruiting posters that depicted demonic German soldiers murdering babies and ravaging innocent women were dismissed as over-zealous propaganda, but were actually not all that far from the truth.

While attending to her duties at the hospital Cavell was introduced to two members of an old aristocratic family, Prince Reginald de Croÿ and his wife, Princess Marie, and they were to have a profound influence on her life. In the autumn of 1914 two Belgian ladies, Henriette Moriame and Louise Thuliez, had been secretly tending wounded English soldiers since the fateful battle of Mons in August. They approached the prince and princess and asked them if they could help find a way to help repatriate the unfortunate troops. A decision was taken to hide them at the De Croÿs' home, Chateau Bellignies, near Mons, where they would be provided with fake passports and a Belgian guide to help them to safety. The secret password for the organization was 'Yorc', the name of Croÿ in reverse.

The chateau soon became a safe haven for English and French soldiers seeking to escape across the border to the Netherlands and eventually back to England. Edith Cavell's Medical Institute became an integral part of this clandestine escape route. In the autumn of 1914, two stranded British soldiers found their way to the Institute where, regardless of the imminent danger, she hid them for two weeks. Others soon followed and every one of them was surreptitiously smuggled out to neutral territory in the Netherlands. Pt. Arthur Wood, one of the soldiers of the 1st Battalion, Norfolk Regiment, who'd fought at the Battle of Mons, recognized a print of Norwich Cathedral on the wall of Cavell's office. She still harboured great affection for her home county. She asked the soldier to take home her Bible and a letter for her mother.

Between November 1914 and July 1915 Cavell was instrumental in helping to organize the repatriation and escape of around 200 people. In order to do this efficiently, she made contact with various secret services and associations. It was incredibly precarious work that demanded nerves of steel and total dedication from all participants. She knew the incredible risk that she was taking, and was fully aware of the dire consequences if she was discovered, but this didn't deter her in the slightest. She regarded the concealment and repatriation of these men as humanitarian acts just as worthy as tending the sick and wounded. Ultimately fastidious and methodical in her work, the men who came to her were asked to sign papers giving their consent for a surgical operation. They were assigned fictitious illnesses, and their names, ages, dates of arrival and departure, and photos of them were all entered in a secret ledger. When the soldiers were spirited away she would write to her mother, describing the men who lodged with her and the guides who led them to safety. In these letters she would obliquely ask for news of their safe arrival in England on the premise that some of the men were relatives of nurses in the school.

The network depended on everyone doing their part, but this was Belgium, a land with divided allegiances. Something was going to give. Two of Cavell's colleagues noticed that she had become more withdrawn and less communicative but they had no idea why. Alongside the escape organization and the increasing difficulties in providing reliable guides and sufficient money for the escapes, her mentor Dr Depage was busy working on the Allied side of the war and his wife Marie had left for America to raise money for the war effort. Marie was drowned on the *Lusitania* when a German U-boat torpedoed the ship on its voyage from America. At around the same time as Marie Depage's death, German secret police began to close in on the escape operations. Their purpose at this juncture was to gather information but they didn't make any arrests until they could ascertain the full extent of the organization's operation and find out who was involved. Cavell was a prime suspect but there still wasn't enough evidence for the police to move in. She was becoming increasingly burdened with running the training school and supervising the building of the new school. She laboured in an atmosphere that was becoming increasingly charged with fear and suspicion. The net was closing.

Cavell's connection to Brussels native Philippe Baucq was widely known inside the organization. Baucq was an active member of the underground who played an important role in disseminating the clandestine newspaper *La Libre Belgique* (*Free Belgium*), and assisted in organizing the *Mot du Soldat* (The soldier's word), a service that provided a communication link between soldiers at the front and their relatives in occupied Belgium. He often worked as a guide, escorting escapees to the Dutch border.

Working in a Red Cross hospital demanded that the wounded of all nations could be treated there indiscriminately and Edith Cavell adhered strictly to this ruling. She had been warned by contacts that it was possible the German authorities were aware of her activities, but this didn't dissuade her from continuing her work. By the early summer of 1915 she was in imminent danger of being arrested. Most biographers believe the real villain in Cavell's story was Frenchman Gaston Quien, later convicted as a collaborator. She wouldn't have noticed that Quien, posing as a wounded French soldier brought in for treatment, was in fact a plant, placed there by the German authorities. Quien had defected to the German side in exchange for his release. Disguised as an Allied soldier in need of safe passage out of the country, he successfully infiltrated the network and passed on enough secret information to implicate Edith Cavell. Aware that the net was closing, she had taken precautions and secretly destroyed any incriminating documents she had in her possession. Precisely how much she knew about the information carried by the men she saved, written on cloth and sewn into clothes, or hidden in shoes, remains a contentious issue to this day.

When Philippe Baucq was arrested in Brussels, a list containing Edith Cavell's name was found in his possession. The die was cast. She was promptly arrested and taken to St Gilles prison, where she remained incarcerated for the next ten weeks, the last two of them in solitary confinement. Her small cell was sparsely furnished, containing a bed, which folded to make a table, a small cupboard and a washbasin. Her nurses sent flowers and she spent her time embroidering and reading her copy of the *Imitation of Christ* that had been sent to her by her friend, Sister Wilkins.

Initially denied visits or legal representation, on 10 September Sadi Kirschen was appointed as her defence lawyer, but he wasn't allowed to visit her or to review the charges and was refused permission to view the trial documents. The specific charge against Cavell, under paragraph 68 of the German military penal code was 'Conducting soldiers to the enemy'. This was a lesser charge than espionage, which carried a death sentence. When questioned, she replied: 'My preoccupation has not been to aid the enemy but to help the men who applied to me to reach the frontier. Once across the frontier they were free.' Technically, she only helped these men get out of Brussels and this should have figured in her trial. Aiding and abetting their escape would have been a less severe charge than the one she was facing. She never denied the charge, but it is widely known that she was a prolific correspondent and the Germans were in possession of a letter that had been recently delivered to her through the American Legation. Even though she was clearly in possession of illegal correspondence, she was never accused of illegally sending or receiving mail. It's also alleged that she openly admitted to the charge against her to avoid being charged with having conducted other seditious activities, which may have incriminated other conspirators. It was to be a closed trial, and neutral observers were not allowed to attend. Five German judges were appointed to try the case, but only the name of the central prosecutor, military judge Eduard Stoebar, a man with a dubious reputation, was made public.

On 7 October 1915, Edith Cavell and other accomplices who worked for the escape network appeared before the military tribunal. It took place in the Belgian Senate Chamber. Determined not to bring her profession into disrepute, Edith Cavell faced her accusers wearing civilian clothes. The trial of all 35 accused took just two days. None of them were allowed decent legal representation. There was no question of Edith being found not guilty. In her painfully honest way she admitted culpability. The only question was the severity of the sentence. The decision was in the hands of the Military Governor of Brussels, General von Sauberzweig, a bitter and vengeful individual who bore a personal grudge against the British because his son had been blinded while fighting them.

The British government appears to have remained passive throughout this whole process. Internal Foreign Office memos record one official assuring colleagues that Mr Brand Whitlock, the 'US minister [in Brussels] will see that she has a fair trial'. Sir Horace Rowland, the FO's top official, agreed. 'I am afraid we are powerless.' The sentiment was echoed by Lord Robert Cecil, who joined the coalition government in 1915 as an under-secretary for foreign affairs after working for the Red Cross. 'Any representation by us,' he advised, 'will do her more harm than good.' They appear to have abandoned Edith Cavell to her fate. Or maybe there was a more sinister reason for their lacklustre approach?

None of the accused was present when, on 11 October 1915, the German judge passed sentence on Edith Cavell, Philippe Baucq, Louise Thulliez, a French teacher from Lille, Countess Jeanne de Belleville and Louis Séverin, a Belgian pharmacist. They were all condemned to death. Others arrested at the same time received varying prison sentences. At 8.30 pm on

11 October, Edith Cavell was informed by the German Army Chaplain, Father Le Seur, of her impending fate and that she had only a few hours left to live. Le Seur was able to arrange a visit by the Anglican Chaplain, Reverend Stirling Gahan. Reverend Gahan arrived at the St Gilles prison at 10.00 pm. Edith Cavell had unfolded her bed and was in her dressing gown. They talked and Edith Cavell said that after so many years of bustling activity she regarded her solitude as cathartic. Stirling Gahan had brought his Communion Set, so together they took the bread and wine and said the Blessing before speaking the words of the hymn *Abide With Me*. Gahan said to her before leaving that, 'We shall always remember you as a heroine and a martyr,' to which she replied: 'Don't think of me like that. Think of me as a nurse who tried to do her duty.'

Stirling Gahan recalled:

'On Monday evening, October 11th, I was admitted by special passport from the German authorities to the prison of St Gilles, where Miss Edith Cavell had been confined for ten weeks. The final sentence had been given early that afternoon.

'To my astonishment and relief I found my friend perfectly calm and resigned. But this could not lessen the tenderness and intensity of feeling on either part during that last interview of almost an hour. Her first words to me were upon a matter concerning herself personally, but the solemn asseveration which accompanied them was made expressly in the light of God and eternity.

'She then added that she wished all her friends to know that she willingly gave her life for her country, and said: "I have no fear nor shrinking; I have seen death so often that it is not strange or fearful to me".'

Frantic appeals for clemency were orchestrated as Hugh Gibson of the American Embassy enlisted the help of the Spanish ambassador, the Marquis de Villalobar, and the Netherlands ambassador, Maurits Van Vollenhoven. General von Sauberzweig had no intention of deviating from the sentence and informed Gibson the executions were scheduled to take place early the following morning.

The US Minister to Belgium Brand Whitlock wrote a personal letter to German Military Governor, Baron von Bissing:

'Your Excellency,
'I have just heard that Miss Cavell, a British subject, and consequently under the protection of my Legation, was this morning condemned to death by court-martial. If my information is correct, the sentence in the present case is more severe than all the others that have been passed in similar cases which have been tried by the same court, and, without going into the reasons for such a drastic sentence, I feel that I have the right to appeal to his Excellency the Governor-General's feelings of humanity and generosity in Miss Cavell's favour, and to ask that the death penalty passed on Miss Cavell may be commuted, and that this unfortunate woman shall not be executed.

'Miss Cavell is the head of the Brussels Surgical Institute. She has spent her life in alleviating the sufferings of others, and her school has turned out many nurses who have watched at the bedside of the sick all the world over, in Germany as in Belgium.

'At the beginning of the war Miss Cavell bestowed her care as freely on the German soldiers as on others. Even in default of all other reasons, her career as a servant of humanity is such as to inspire the greatest sympathy and to call for pardon.

'If the information in my possession is correct, Miss Cavell, far from shielding herself, has, with commendable straightforwardness, admitted the truth of all the charges against her, and it is the very information which she herself has furnished, and which she alone was in a position to furnish, that has aggravated the severity of the sentence passed on her. It is then with confidence, and in the hope of its favourable reception, that I beg your Excellency to submit to the Governor-General my request for pardon on Miss Cavell's behalf.'

Edith Cavell was executed by firing squad on 12 October 1915. She is often erroneously depicted wearing a nursing uniform when she was executed, but this was pure propaganda.

The allies used Cavell's execution as propaganda for the purpose of recruitment. The truth was she died with great dignity, displaying incredible courage and fortitude right to the very end.

Edith Cavell was 49 years old. She remained magnanimous even when facing imminent death, forgiving her executioners, even willing to admit the justice of their sentence. Her last words according to Father Le Seur were, 'My conscience is clear. I die for God and my country.' Stories circulated that the execution squad fired wide and that she fainted and was finally put to death by a German officer. This is pure conjecture, because reliable witness accounts make no reference to this at all. Across the British Empire her death was used to galvanize public opinion against the Germans. It's maybe cynical but probably true to suggest that Edith Cavell was worth more to the British dead than alive in terms of her propaganda value. In Britain, recruitment numbers rose from 5,000 to 10,000 a week following her execution. The frenzy of outrage and condemnation that it provoked around the world was unprecedented.

Recently uncovered evidence suggests that she may indeed have worked as a spy, while further British documents indicate that the German authorities acted in accordance with the law when they sentenced her to death. Edith Cavell deserves to be remembered as a heroine even if she was a spy.

CHAPTER ELEVEN

HEMINGWAY'S INSPIRATION

It would take a lot of imagination to describe Ernest Hemingway as angelic, even if he did work for the Red Cross. In 1917, a hormonally challenged young man from Illinois called Ernest Miller Hemingway left his job at the *Kansas City Star* newspaper and signed on as an ambulance driver with the American Red Cross. He was 18, eager for adventure and responding to a recruitment drive. Actually, there was more to it than that. He had tried to enlist in the army, but had been rejected due to poor vision. Undeterred, he decided he would get to the front. Rudyard Kipling's son Jack was almost blind but that didn't stop his father from getting him a commission in the Irish Guards. The difference was that Ernest didn't have any masonic connections, but what he did have was a pure, undiluted determination to join the fray and get stuck in. As far as Ernest was concerned the location of the front was superfluous, the fight was on and he wanted to somehow be a part of it. He had even written to his sister explaining that he had plans to join the Canadian Army. In desperation he had joined a National Guard unit, which appears to have placated his parents to some extent, but not him. The criteria for admission to the National Guard was considerably less stringent than the army, the only problem was that they weren't earmarked for overseas duty. Nevertheless, the 2nd Missouri Home Guards regiment would be able to provide young Ernest with some rudimentary military experience.

During those first turbulent years in World War I, President Wilson had struggled to preserve American neutrality. This had been emphasized in 1916 on his re-election campaign slogan that proclaimed, 'He kept us out of war'. By early 1917, the British naval blockade of the Continent and German submarine warfare increasingly compromised the president's anti-war stance and, finally, on 6 April the United States declared war on Germany. That day, the American Red Cross (ARC) shunned its neutrality and assumed its other federally chartered military role to provide medical assistance to the country's armed forces in wartime. It looked good on paper, but in reality, just like the US armed forces, the organization was drastically ill-prepared for the role it was assuming. It's entirely possible that Ernest saw the ARC as a possible vehicle to get to the front faster than the army. Six base hospitals had already been dispatched to support the British Expeditionary Force in May 1917. Most, if not all, of these Red Cross hospitals were already operating as American-sponsored independent institutions even before America's entry into the war. The first of these to be appropriated by the army and ARC was the American Ambulance Hospital in Paris. The order came directly from Major General 'Black Jack' John J. Pershing, commander of the American Expeditionary Force.

According to one version of Ernest Hemingway's account, one day a wire service story came to the telegraph desk dealing with the Red Cross's need for volunteers to work with the Italian Army. Being the impetuous young man that he was, Ernest cabled his application before the paper even had a chance to publish the item. This was a barometer of how eager he was for adventure. He was no different from countless other young men who had signed up, fired with patriotic zeal, testosterone, temporary insanity and a determination to 'do their bit'.

In 1917 the Italian Army had suffered a crushing defeat inflicted by the Austro-Hungarian and German forces at a place called Caporetto. Italian Army casualties were unprecedented, estimated between 700,000 and 750,000. During the final three months of 1917 the enemy had taken 335,000 prisoners, including those belonging to labour battalions and those hospitalized soldiers left to their fate as the Italian Army retreated. Austro-Hungarian troops occupied 5,200 sq km (2,000 sq miles) of Italian soil and had confiscated millions of pounds of supplies. The aspirations of the Central Powers to take Italy out of the war completely had almost succeeded. They had won a great victory and had caused much uneasiness, not only in Italy but among the Allies as a whole. The situation was nearing desperation and the Allies had serious reservations as to whether the Italian Army would be able to recover.

While Italian forces were regrouping and replacing men and equipment lost at Caporetto, US Captain George Utassy, who had recently been appointed administrative officer at the Italian field headquarters in charge of all ambulance units in Italy, issued a strong appeal. 'One hundred Americans are needed at once by the American Red Cross for ambulance service behind the Italian lines.' The wording of the article was unambiguous: 'It is a splendid opportunity for men of independent means, over draft age, who are strong and healthy and able to drive automobiles. Consideration will be given to men 25 years or over, who are exempt for minor defects. All cost of equipment and living expenses abroad will be covered by the American Red Cross, and transportation expenses will be paid, if necessary.'

The eventual response was overwhelming and resulted in a flood of applicants. Ernest saw this as his opportunity and he wasn't going to let it slip. He had heard, and possibly read, the rousing sermons of Dr William Barton of the First Congregational Church, encouraging America's young men to go to war, but these didn't necessarily inspire Ernest's burgeoning sense of adventure. The sister of this minister was Clara Barton, the woman who had originally founded the Red Cross in America.

Once Ernest's application had been approved, he left Kansas to join the Red Cross in New York on 12 May 1918. When the train pulled into Grand Central Station he had roughly ten days to acclimatize to his new role as a Red Cross volunteer before boarding the steamship that would take him overseas. His initiation into the Red Cross in New York coincided with a peak of support for the beleaguered Italians as they anticipated further enemy offensives that summer. While Ernest was in New York the mayor, John F. Hylan, announced the opening of Red Cross Week, scheduled to start on 20 May.

Two days before the commencement of various Red Cross fundraising and PR activities, thousands of war workers had paraded through Manhattan amid a milling throng of spectators. Ernest, who hadn't yet fired a shot in anger or touched foot on foreign soil, had no problem participating in the parade. Unencumbered by not having actually done anything useful for the Red Cross, he even wrote a letter home about the attention he and his organization received during the pageant: 'We paraded 85 blocks down 5th Ave today and were reviewed by President Wilson. About 75,000 were in line and we were the star attraction.' A few days later, on 23 May, after a few minor delays, he was aboard the steamship *Chicago* heading to Bordeaux. He wasn't very complimentary about the vessel, describing it as 'the rottenest tub in the world'. It was a relatively uneventful crossing of the Atlantic because, by that time in 1918, the danger of being attacked by German U-boats was highly unlikely. This fact appears to have disappointed Ernest somewhat because in his anticipation of partaking in some action he had strolled the decks each day hoping to spot a U-boat. By the time the ship docked in Bordeaux on 1 June he felt that he'd been defrauded.

The one thing he did achieve during the voyage was making new friends. Seemingly endless alcohol-fuelled poker games and shooting craps helped him interact with his shipmates. This was more in tune with the developing character of the Ernest Hemingway that the world would eventually come to know. The *esprit de corps* that he established with two of these men endured through his service until well after the Great War had ended.

So, there he was in France and ready for adventure. A few days after his arrival on the French mainland he was on a train heading to the city of love, Paris. He appears to have been captivated and enthralled by European culture, and that first visit to Paris would initiate a love affair with the city that would endure for decades. He quickly registered at 'Number Four', the Red Cross headquarters on the Place de la Concord. It was a luxurious former palace complete with ornate crystal chandeliers, red carpets and high ceilings that must have seriously impressed the young man from Kansas, unaccustomed to such luxury and comfort. He wasn't given any immediate tasks so those first days were donated to pure hedonistic pursuits such as getting to know the city and checking out all of the major attractions.

*   *   *

While he was there the Germans lobbed over some high velocity shells from their feared 'Big Bertha' Howitzer 114 km (71 miles) away. The first attack occurred on Good Friday, 1918, and continued thereafter. The gun was capable of firing a 106 kg (234 lb) shell to a range of around 130 km (80 miles). A total of around 320 to 367 shells were fired, at a maximum rate of roughly 20 per day. The shells killed 250 people, wounded 620, and caused considerable damage to property. The name Big Bertha was applied by members of the Allied forces to these extreme long-range cannons that were better known locally simply as the 'Paris Guns'. Blasé Parisians were generally unfazed by these regular bombardments and went about their lives as normal. This appears to have inspired the thrill-seeking Ernest, who actually hired taxis so he could inspect the shell craters made by these big guns.

He finally left Paris on an overnight train that arrived in Milan on Friday, 7 June. As soon as he got there he was exposed to the brutal reality of war when an explosion occurred in a storage area at a nearby munitions factory. Ernest and his colleagues were transported to the site to assist in collecting dead bodies and other remains that littered the countryside. This wasn't the frontline and most of the victims were women but it would have been a gruesome introduction nonetheless. Two days later he was finally where he wanted to be, in proximity to the frontlines. The Red Cross post at Schio had 36 Red Cross ambulance drivers and was located at the base of the Little Dolomites, a few miles from the Austrian positions. It was nowhere near the Piave River, where some of the most intense action developed during June and July of that year.

Ernest and authority was not a particularly great combination and he complained vociferously about his captain there from day one. Captain Bates was a veteran of many great World War I battles. He was a strict disciplinarian who valued his role supervising the drivers and managing the vehicles. He often conducted personal reconnaissance of the front in preparation for major offensives and made frequent visits to check the conduct of his volunteers. His insistence on exemplary behaviour by his personnel at all times didn't endear him to them. By the same token, Ernest wasn't all that popular with some of his fellow volunteers either who criticized his impatience to experience frontline action. Devoid of any serious activity and with a pool of 18 pairs of drivers operating in shifts lasting two or three days, it is unlikely that he would have been called upon to sit behind the steering wheel of an ambulance other than to pose for a photograph. Consequently, he set the parameters for his future image, passing his time drinking copious amounts of alcohol, gambling, fighting and attempting to impress some of the local ladies.

The Austrians launched a major offensive on 15 June with a massive but predicted bombardment and once the fighting kicked in it didn't engage the services of Ernest's Section 4 unit in Schio. He supplemented some of his time writing flippant articles for the Section 4 self-printed monthly magazine called *Ciao*, but things were about to change. On 24 June he was finally presented with an opportunity to participate in some action, but it wouldn't have much to do with driving an ambulance. Volunteers were requested to staff canteens in proximity to the frontlines and Ernest immediately took one step forward. He joined a unit that reached forward areas using canteens mounted on wheels that became known as 'rolling kitchens'. It sounded like a good idea at the time but it didn't take long before Ernest began complaining that he should be driving an ambulance instead of handing out cigarettes and chocolate.

At least now he had the chance to see battle conditions up close. When he arrived at the most active combat zone along that front, the Austrians had already been defeated in the Battle of the Piave and the Italians were in the midst of launching their counterattack. As the Austrians retreated, he travelled on some of the same roads and finally got to satiate his thirst by witnessing scenes of terrible carnage and devastation. Shortly after this he would experience a little more than he had bargained for, when he was severely wounded. He had succeeded in getting closer to the action and was incongruously using a bicycle to distribute his supplies of tobacco and confectionary to frontline Italian troops at a place called Fossalta. Suddenly, an enemy mortar shell exploded nearby, showering shrapnel into Ernest and three Italian soldiers. One was killed outright and another severely wounded, while Ernest absorbed hundreds of pieces of metal into his legs, scrotum and lower abdomen. Despite his horrific wounds he displayed remarkable endurance and courage, carrying one of the wounded soldiers 50 yards before he was hit in the leg by machine gun fire. Even this didn't knock him off his feet and he somehow managed to progress a further 100 yards before he blacked out. It was a tremendous display of resilience in terrifying conditions. Apart from the physical wounds the event left an

Nurse Kurowsky provided pugnacious author Ernest Hemingway's inspiration for his novel From Here to Eternity.

indelible stain on his mind that would remain with him for the rest of his life. It wouldn't, however, deter him from seeking other wars, other battles and other conflicts.

During his subsequent six months of convalescence Ernest fell head over heels in love with an American Red Cross nurse, Agnes von Kurowsky. He would go on to recount the incident and transpose versions of his experiences through literary classics such as *A Farewell to Arms*. Agnes von Kurowsky was 26 and Ernest 18 when they first met and the age difference clearly influenced their brief relationship. She was the inspiration for the character of Catherine Barkley, the tragic heroine of *A Farewell to Arms*. Agnes did not reciprocate Ernest's passion, and five months after their first meeting she flatly rejected his marriage proposal. Their love affair came to an abrupt end when Ernest returned to the US and she unceremoniously dumped him for an Italian officer.

Many years later he recounted some of his experiences in *Men at War*, a compilation of 82 war stories from around the world. He wrote:

'When you go to war as a boy you have a great illusion of immortality. Other people get killed not you. Then when you are badly wounded the first time you lose that illusion and you know it can happen to you. After being severely wounded two weeks before my nineteenth birthday I had a bad time until I figured out that nothing could happen to me that had not happened to all men before me. Whatever I had to do men had always done. If they had done it then I could do it too and the best thing was not to worry about it.'

It's entirely possible that due to his service with the National Guard he could have eventually been selected for the regular army despite his problematic eyesight, but the Red Cross was a more immediate solution for one so impatient. Ernest Hemingway was, however, one of the first Americans to receive a commendation in World War I when the Italian government presented him with the Silver Medal of Valour. He had earned it and he deserved it. He went on to write several literary masterpieces. He took his own life on 2 July 1961, in Ketchum, Idaho. He was Ernest Hemingway.

CHAPTER TWELVE

OUR NELLIE AND OTHER WORLD WAR I NURSES

Nellie was the first-born child of George and Elizabeth Spindler. Born in Wakefield, West Yorkshire, in 1891, her father was a sergeant in the Wakefield City Police Force. By 1911, George, who had a reputation for excellent first aid skills, had risen to the rank of inspector and Nellie had trained as a nurse at Township Infirmary in Leeds. She completed her training in 1915, and it's possible that her Roman Catholic faith and the example of public service set by her father may have influenced her future life and career choices. Meanwhile, she was working at a local hospital and living away from home, but not too far that she couldn't pop over to partake of the Sunday roast when she wasn't working. The Spindler family lived in relative comfort during the ostentatious reign of King Edward VII. Life was good.

On 1 August 1914 the Germans declared war on France, and had every intention of taking Paris quickly to remove France as a threat to their war aims in the West. On the same day, the German government demanded passage through Belgium to allow them to sweep around the French border fortifications protecting Paris from the north. Albert I, King of Belgium, responded to this threat by asking the British to honour their treaty to support his country in the event of invasion. Britain would not renege on its obligation to poor little Belgium. It appeared that the peace, so widely enjoyed by the stylish Edwardians, was in danger of coming to an abrupt end when a few days later Great Britain fulfilled its obligation and declared war on Germany.

The announcement was greeted with an outburst of unprecedented patriotic fervour as thousands of naïve, enthusiastic young men responded to Lord Kitchener's iconic 'Your Country Needs You' poster. Within just eight weeks, over 750,000 men had rallied to the call and joined a huge volunteer citizens' army. In order to boost figures the British government organized the Parliamentary Recruitment Committee (PRC), which circulated leaflets and posters, and organized mass rallies and numerous other public events. Considerable social pressure was applied to those men who didn't volunteer, and they risked vilification as cowards. They could even be accosted in the

The terrible Battle of Passchendaele was the backdrop to nurse Nellie Spindler's untimely death.

street by pretty young ladies and unceremoniously presented with a white feather. It was a time of colourful, boisterous brass bands marching down high streets at the head of parades, bolstered by the support of the townsfolk. Meanwhile, music hall stars of the day appeared in theatres with a single purpose, to entice young men to fight and die for their country.

In the north, where young Nellie lived, the response was initially more subdued. This was the dour, industrial heart of the British Empire, home to the coalmines, steel works, docksides and 'dark satanic mills'. It would be a little more difficult to persuade its hard-working young men that this was going to be the 'war to end all wars', or that it would 'all be over by Christmas'. Many of the jobs in these areas fell into the government-assigned Reserved Occupation category, meaning the workers doing them didn't have to go to the front.

But that didn't stop some people thinking about it. These were cities of soot-blackened stone surrounded by endless, faceless rows of terraced houses shrouded in choking smog belching belligerently from the chimneys of local mines and factories. Life was hard and short. Maybe, some menfolk thought, going to war was a potential escape, a reasonable alternative to the drudgery of their lives.

The confrontations and battles of those first few months of World War I were so damaging to the British Army that replacements were badly needed. Eventually conscripts would replace the volunteers. During this period the police and fire service were given notice of being called up and some had to attend medical examinations in readiness. There was also a call for young women needed as nurses. Nellie was one such woman, a trained nurse who answered the nation's call and joined the Queen Alexandra's Imperial Military Nursing Service (QAIMNS). In the first weeks of the war the QAIMNS were mobilized for duty with the British Expeditionary Force (BEF). There were just 3,000 nurses in 1914; by 1918 this number had risen to 23,000.

Those indomitable nurses who served on the Western Front were quick to improvise when the first deadly clouds of gas floated toward the Allied positions on 10 March 1915 at Ypres, in Belgium. The Germans flagrantly discharged 168 tonnes of chlorine gas from strategically placed cylinders. The deathly cloud drifted toward Allied trenches, inflicting over 5,000 casualties. In the absence of respirators, the nurses drenched their sanitary towels in *eau de cologne* and held them over their faces and those of the wounded soldiers.

While the horrors of World War I unfolded, Nellie began working as a staff nurse at the Whittington Military Hospital at Lichfield, Staffordshire, before being posted to the British Army, joining Queen Alexandra's Imperial Military Nursing Service in Le Havre, France, in May 1917.

These incredibly brave women were volunteers, they went wherever they were sent, were present in all the theatres of war, and in many cases faced similar dangers to those of the soldiers in or near the frontlines. Nellie, along with other nurses, worked in one of the Casualty Clearing Stations (CCS). These Clearing Stations were usually a safe distance from the front, and normally comprised large tents, some containing up to 800 beds. A typical CCS could hold up to 1,000 casualties at any time, and would normally admit 15–30 cases in rotation. At peak times of battle, even the CCSs often became inundated with casualties. Serious operations such as limb amputations were carried out here. Some CCSs were specialist units designated for nervous disorders, skin diseases, infectious diseases and certain other types of wounds. They didn't move location very often, and the infrastructure of railways usually dictated their location. Most evacuated casualties came away from the CCS by rail, although motor ambulances and canal barges also carried casualties to Base Hospitals, or directly to a port of embarkation if the man had been identified as a 'Blighty' case, that is having a wound that guaranteed a ticket home. The term shell shock is most readily associated with World War I, but scant attention was paid to those who exhibited symptoms of this condition at the time. The original assumption was that being too close to an exploding shell had the potential to cause dysfunctional behaviours. Nevertheless, a soldier displaying neuropsychiatric symptoms yet showing no physical damage could errantly be accused of cowardice and sentenced to death as a warning to other 'malingerers'. During the war, 17 British soldiers were executed for cowardice. All have since been officially pardoned.

The 44th CCS, situated in the tiny Belgian village of Brandhoek in Flanders, is where Nellie was stationed in the summer of 1917. It was positioned next to a railway and precariously close to a munitions dump.

The 44th CCS specialized in abdominal wounds that needed to be treated with the utmost urgency due to blood loss. They toiled under terrible conditions, removing filthy, blood-encrusted uniforms, monitoring vitals, debriding, suturing and dressing horrendous wounds while caring for the dying. It was no job for the faint-hearted.

On 31 July 1917 the terrible Battle of Passchendaele began. The Allied assault was launched in the early hours. At the 44th CCS, as the first deafening artillery barrages were released, steel instruments clattered in enamel trays and pendulous saline drips swung erratically while the very earth shook and trembled beneath the feet of the staff. The sturdiest of constitutions would have been shaken to the core, but Nellie was a Yorkshire lass made of sterner stuff. Two newly arrived nurses cowered and recoiled every time shells landed in close proximity, but Nellie just went about her business, ran a finger inside her starched collar and adjusted the metal-framed glasses that were perpetually slipping down her nose

A Casualty Clearing Station in World War I was located behind the front lines just beyond the range of enemy artillery and often in proximity to transportation facilities.

from the perspiration. Within hours of the first attacks the CCS became overwhelmed with casualties.

In a matter of days the constant shelling combined with the heaviest rain for 30 years annihilated the delicate centuries-old Flemish drainage systems and churned the clay soil into a pungent quagmire of thick yellow mud that clogged up rifles and immobilized tanks. Men and horses drowned in foul-smelling shell craters, while artillery pieces and vehicles would slowly sink from sight while soldiers looked on impotently. This was the hell of Passchendaele.

Nellie's final letter home, beautifully written in her meticulous copperplate hand, arrived at Stanley Road, Eastmoor, in Wakefield, in early August 1917, and contained a small, silver pendant embossed with the figure of a weeping angel intended as a present for her sister, Lily. It was dated 28 July 1917. This was typically the kind of thing Nellie sent home. She was after all a deeply religious young woman who spent what scant free time she had visiting local churches.

The morning of 21 August 1917 was a day like any other on the Western Front. Artillery exchanges began at around 10.00 am and two shells just missed the living quarters of the CCS nurses. Percussion from the blasts caused the walls of the vast canvas wards to billow and swell like the sails of a three-masted man-of-war. In the distance, the nursing staff could hear the spitting, tremulous blasts of machine gun fire harvesting death in no man's land, and ultimately adding to the already overburdened workload. Outside, medical orderlies and stretcher-bearers flinched as they unloaded their latest cargo of blood, pain and misery. Young grimy faces with wild eyes, some walking and some lying down, were escorted to the triage ward as yet more shells rained indiscriminately down around the hospital.

Nellie left the ward that night exhausted and prepared for a restorative night's sleep. She hadn't been in her little camp bed long when suddenly there was a blinding flash as a shell impacted the nurse's quarters. When the dust settled it revealed a scene of total carnage. Bloodied limbs and torsos lay around and in the far corner of the tent a young nurse attempted but failed to lift herself from the ground. Her glasses had been blown from her face and a dark red stain was spreading across her heaving chest. Nellie had been hit by a piece of shrapnel that had entered her diminutive frame from behind, narrowly missing her heart. Other nurses quickly ran to her aid, but despite frantic attempts to save her life it was all to no avail. Within minutes she had slipped from consciousness and less than 20 minutes later she was pronounced dead. That same day the CSS was relocated to a place called Lijssenthoek, near Poperinge. Nurse Kate Luard, who was the sister in charge of the adjacent 32nd CCS, later described the catastrophic events:

'The business began about 10 a.m. Two came pretty close after each other and both just cleared us and No. 44. The third crashed between Sister E's ward in our lines and the Sisters' Quarters of No. 44. Bits came over everywhere, pitching at one's feet as we rushed to the scene of the action, and one just missed one of my Night Sisters getting into bed in our Compound. I knew by the crash where it must have gone and found Sister E. as white as paper but smiling happily and comforting the terrified patients. Bits tore through her Ward but hurt no one. Having to be thoroughly jovial to the patients on these occasions helps us considerably ourselves.

'Then I came on to the shell-hole and the wrecked tents in the Sister's Quarters at 44. A group of stricken M.O.'s were standing about and in one tent the Sister was dying. The piece went through her from back to front near her heart. She was only conscious a few minutes and only lived 20 minutes. She was in bed asleep. The Sister who shared her tent had been sent down the day before because she couldn't stand the noise and the day and night conditions. The Sister who should have been in the tent, which was nearest, was out for a walk or she would have been blown to bits; everything in her tent was; so it was in my empty Ward next to Sister E. It all made one feel sick.'

Sister Nellie Spindler was buried with full military honours at the Lijssenthoek cemetery, the only woman among the graves of 10,800 men. Lest we forget.

Alice Ross King was a nurse at the 2nd Australian Casualty Clearing Station, which was situated close to the battlefront near Trois Arbres in

France during World War I. One night she heard the terrifying whistle of incoming bombs. Moments later one of the missiles exploded directly in front of her, knocking her clean off her feet. Alice looked around for the orderly but couldn't see him. Realizing the enormity of the situation, she immediately rushed back to her patients. As the deadly projectiles began to explode among the buildings and tents she ran to the wards, where she discovered what was left of the pneumonia tent. An extract from her diary reads: 'Though I shouted, nobody answered me or I could hear nothing for the roar of the planes and artillery. I seemed to be the only living thing about. I kept calling for the orderly to help me and thought he was funking, but the poor boy had been blown to bits.'

The indefatigable nurse Alice Ross King was an Australian civilian and military nurse who participated in both World Wars. Australia's most decorated woman, she was always a great source of inspiration to her colleagues.

Struggling under the collapsed canvas of the tent and in partial darkness, she attempted to lift a delirious patient from the floor: 'I had my right arm under a leg which I thought was his but when I lifted [it] I found to my horror that it was a loose leg with a boot and a puttee on it. One of the orderly's legs had been blown off and had landed on the patient's bed. Next day they found the trunk up a tree about twenty yards away.'

In the ensuing hours, Alice displayed incredible courage and paid little attention to her own safety. Sometime later, after being promoted to head sister, Alice moved to an advanced dressing station just behind the front lines. The stream of incoming wounded seemed endless and the days were long and arduous. After one punishing shift, when the staff appeared to be finally gaining the upper hand, the doctor in charge told Alice to get some rest. As she made her way back to her tent, she heard the feeble, anguished moans of wounded men. She looked for and found the source: 53 badly wounded German prisoners who hadn't been attended for three days. Irrespective that they were enemy wounded, Alice immediately called for the doctor. Her diary entry reads: 'I shall never forget the cries that greeted me. They had gone without food or water. Everyone on our staff was deadbeat but I got the doctor to come and fix them up. We did forty patients in 45 minutes (the other 13 had died). No waiting for chloroform, amputations and all, and onto the train an hour and a half after I had found them.'

For her bravery and devotion to duty she was awarded the AIF Military Medal and the Royal Red Cross, 2nd Class.

As well as Alice, there were innumerable other heroes, many of them unsung, who braved bullets and bombs to perform their duties.

During the cataclysmic Champagne-Marne Operation that began on 15 July 1918, there was a mobile hospital unit precariously close to the frontline. Captain Fordyce St John, Commander of Mobile Hospital No. 2, wrote:

'During the first two hours of the barrage, the shells were landing approximately 125 yards beyond us and causing no trouble but at about six in the morning the enemy changed his range and the shells began dropping short and long, the typical range-finding method used, and it was now impossible for the wounded to reach us. This situation continued until seven o'clock, when high explosives began falling among the thin wooden sheds of the hospital itself, so that it became necessary to issue an order to evacuate the wards and to remove all patients to the underground dugout. Before this could be accomplished, the shock ward was pretty well demolished by two direct hits. Several casualties had already occurred, and, before the shacks could be evacuated, two more men were killed, one of whom was decapitated. A Presbyterian Hospital nurse in charge of this ward was dragged protesting from her post forty seconds before the shell hit the frail building. Patients were being killed as they were unloaded from ambulances.'

One young officer present at the Battle of Loos in 1915 wrote: 'I saw vague, spectral figures through the haze responding to the pitiful cries of wounded soldiers. While crouching low, sometimes crawling over the dismembered remnants of those recently taken, they braved bullets and bombs to perform their duties. How could one not be impressed?' They were lifesavers and angels of mercy who paid the ultimate price on many occasions. More often than not their deeds would be forgotten, cast aside while others reaped the credit for a battle won or a successful assault on enemy positions.

There is not much information out there about German nurses who served in World War I, but one particular nurse recorded some of her experiences. Paula Jung was born in September 1893 in Wuppertal-Barmen, the second of four children. Spurred on by patriotic speeches, posters and an irrepressible sense of adventure, she decided to enrol as a nurse and go to the front. In Kaiser Wilhelm II's Germany such ambitions were not encouraged. In this polarized society women stayed at home and did domestic chores; they didn't go to battle zones and risk their lives because war was a strictly male domain. As the years passed and German casualties mounted, this misogynistic view of women's roles in war had to adapt to meet the demand for qualified nurses. Paula was just one of thousands of young women who took the opportunity to escape the claustrophobic social constraints of the day, even if they had no idea what they were getting into. Paula's parents objected vociferously to their daughter's choice of profession and her ambition to serve the fatherland. She politely listened to their heartfelt objections and impassioned reasons, and then with Teutonic determination packed her suitcase and promptly left home.

She completely applied herself to her medical training, which included among other things horse riding lessons and instruction on how to steer a horse-drawn cart. Fast forward two years and by the end of 1917 Paula was just behind the lines on the Western Front, where she remained until the end of the war on 11 November 1918. She saw service at Ypres and Arras. Every now and then she sent home a letter or two. She was very careful not to cause her parents any unnecessary distress and consequently the letters read like inane 'wish you were here' holiday postcards. She would send home photographs of her posing with other nurses in impeccably white starched uniforms. She never mentioned the daily horrors she witnessed and even had the temerity to sign the letters 'from your sister Paula beneath the thunderous guns'.

She did, however, keep a small diary that provides a short but illuminating insight into the everyday life of frontline nurses. While serving near Langemarck in Ypres she heard that her brother, Arthur, had been wounded and was recuperating in a nearby hospital. This is where those seemingly useless horse-riding lessons came in handy because she borrowed a carthorse and rode over to see him in the middle of the night. On the card that she wrote home to her parents she abandoned some of her Teutonic stoicism: 'I hope that you have a good Pentecost. I went to see Arthur and during my journey back to my quarters I witnessed a terrible bombardment by enemy pilots. I thought I would never see any of you again.'

After the war, Paula married dentist Georg Geller and had four children. It was only later on in life that she opened up and spoke of her wartime experiences. Whereas most mothers would have told comforting bedtime tales, Paula regaled her children with stories about seriously wounded, blood-stained young men who called for their mothers while clinging desperately to life in overcrowded hospitals. She also told them about the religious soldiers who would pray in an attempt to assuage their painful despair, and the innumerable medical interventions that were carried out by the experienced nurses themselves, even though they were not officially authorized to do so.

Paula kept her Flanders Cross medal and other honours in a special box for her grandchildren. One particular item inspired the curiosity of her grandson. It was a shard of metal. This jagged piece of scrap iron, roughly 2 cm (¾ in) long, was the remains of a Mills grenade that had almost severed Paula's finger and embedded itself in the wall behind her head. 'Two centimetres closer and I would have been killed outright,' she would impart with worrying jocularity. Then she would hold up the afflicted crooked index finger as proof. Oh, what a lovely war!

Another notable World War I nurse who worked in Allied hospitals was Julia C. Stimson, born in Worcester, Massachusetts, on 26 May 1881. She attended the Brearley School in New York City for her preliminary education and went on to Vassar College, graduating in 1901. In 1908, she graduated from the New York Hospital Training School for Nurses and received her diploma. Shortly after, she became Superintendent of Nurses at Harlem Hospital. On 15 May 1917 Stimson sailed to Europe as a member of the Army Nurses Corps and Chief Nurse of Base Hospital 21, the St Louis Unit. Between 18 May and 3 June, six fully equipped American Base Hospitals landed at the ports of Liverpool and Falmouth in England. A grateful British government gave them a courteous welcome. Once in England, contingents from the soon-to-be-augmented British military hospitals in France travelled from the Continent to meet with the new arrivals and to assist them in their movement to France. Beginning on 24 May and continuing through 11 June, the six Base Hospitals transited to France to begin their service with the British Expeditionary Forces. These American physicians, nurses and enlisted men would face the possibility of death and destruction months before the first American soldiers would see combat. US medical personnel were the first of their countrymen and women to deploy and the first to suffer casualties.

Julia Stimson had also arrived at Liverpool and was stationed at Base Hospital 21 in France, where she served the hospital group until April 1918, when she was assigned the duties of the Head of all Nurses associated with the American Red Cross Nurses in France. In December, she also became Director of Nursing Service of the American Expeditionary Forces (AEF) and was in charge of the Army Nurses Corps.

Like some of her predecessors she was a dedicated feminist and, in many ways, a reformer, a pioneer, who during her lifetime raised the bar of American nursing considerably. When she became superintendent of the Army Nurses Corps, among other things she elevated the level of requirements for appointment to the corps, instigated more rigid physical examinations and instituted statistical studies and proper reporting. She sailed for Europe on 15 May 1917, as appointed chief nurse of Base Hospital 21 located near Rouen. This unit was composed chiefly of doctors and nurses associated with Washington University and Barnes Hospital in St Louis. The British Expeditionary Force in France primarily used it. Stimson remained with it until April 1918, when she was assigned to duty with the American Red Cross in Paris.

Victims of a tear gas attack in April 1918. Poison gas was first used in World War I by the Germans at Ypres, 22 April 1915.

Her proud father compiled a book of her wartime letters home, which he entitled *Finding Themselves*. It was published in 1918 and although it was lauded by the popular press, not everyone was impressed. Some of the nurses Stimson had led in France found the title offensive. They felt its wording suggested that Stimson saw herself at a distance from them, operating on a higher level.

Julia reacted to the nurses' objections in a letter she wrote home to her parents at Christmas in 1918. It had caused her some distress to acknowledge that some of the other nurses had taken umbrage at what was a rather innocuous title. She wrote an impassioned letter to her parents about some of the effects of chemical warfare that she witnessed at the hospital in France: 'Our nurses don't need any "Hate Lecture" after what we have seen in the past few days. We have been receiving patients that have been gassed, and burned in a most mysterious way. Their clothing is not burned at all, but they have bad burns on their bodies, on parts that are covered by clothing. The doctors think it has been done by some chemical that gets its full action on the skin after it is moist, and when the men sweat, it is in these places that are the most moist that the burns are the worst. The Germans have been using a kind of oil in bombs, the men say it is oil of mustard. These bombs explode and the men's eyes, noses, and throats are so irritated they do not detect the poison gas fumes that come from the bombs that follow these oil ones, and so they either inhale it and die like flies, or have a delayed action and are affected by it terribly several hours later. We have had a lot of these delayed-action gassed men, who cough and cough continuously, like children with whooping cough. We had a very bad case the other night who had not slept one hour for four nights or days, and whose coughing paroxysms came every minute and a half by the clock. When finally the nurses got him to sleep, after rigging up a croup tent over him so that he could breathe steam from a croup kettle over a little stove that literally had to be held in the hands to make it burn properly, they said they were ready to get down on their knees in gratitude, his anguish had been so terrible to watch.'

She directed the activities of 10,000 army nurses during the final days of the war and through the difficult post-war demobilization period. Thanks to her dedication and her efforts, thousands of wounded soldiers received good medical care. For her service in France during the war, the United States government awarded Stimson the Distinguished Service Medal. Other nations bestowed the British Royal Red Cross, 1st Class; the French *Medaille de la Reconnaissance Francaise*; the *Medaille d'Honneur de l'Hygiene Publique*; and the International Red Cross 'Florence Nightingale' Medal. After the war she continued to work as a nurse and was a key recruiter of female nurses in World War II.

Among other things, the Great War went a long way to redefining class restrictions on both sides of the Atlantic, which up until 1917 had prevented privileged young women from even considering the prospect of employment in the nursing profession. Patriotism was a great leveller. One socialite called Winifred Tittman, the daughter of a prominent St Louis family, recalled a half century later: 'Once my brother was shot down, I was allowed to go to nursing school.' Army nurses were presented with military medals for bravery and some even died for their country, but they were not granted actual military rank until 1920. Even then, the conferred title didn't allow them the same privileges as commissioned ranks.

When America entered the war in April 1917, the army's need for nurses was so desperate that a voluntary aide system was even considered. Despite the army's aspiration to enrol more nurses, military authorities didn't provide them with the same benefits afforded to other branches even when they were discharged from service. On top of this the pecuniary dissimilarities between serving men and women only served to reinforce Julia Stimson's feminist ideologies.

Another notable World War I nurse that pre-empted American involvement was Isabel Anderson. She was the wife of US Ambassador Larz Anderson, the American envoy to Belgium from 1911 to 1912. When the call came she was one of the thousands of women who volunteered to help in the war effort. At home in the US, she raised funds for war-related charities before volunteering to work for the American Red Cross in field hospitals directly behind the front lines. She remained there for eight months. For her service she was awarded the French *Croix de Guerre* and the Belgian Queen Elisabeth Medal for her work. In her book *Zigzagging* she relates some of her experiences as a frontline nurse. Her experience living as the wife of a US ambassador in Brussels had provided Isabel with a decent knowledge of the French language and this proved to be an advantage when she was at the front, as she sometimes showed in her letters:

'My first day, a handsome man with thick black hair and big black eyes was brought in right from the trenches. He had both legs cut off, but fortunately, he did not know it. I stayed by his bedside most of the time after he came out of the ether, but he died at ten that night. I became especially interested the next day in a little blond man who had been wounded three times and given every kind of decoration. He died that evening. After this I was so exhausted and sad that I hardly slept, and cried most of the night. Then I caught cold in my side, and blistered it with iodine. Indeed, I was discouraged, but kept going and didn't lose an hour's work.

'In the ward we gave salt injections and morphine shots, etc., and had blood transfusions. I mixed every known kind of drink, and fetched and carried, and made *bandages de corps*, and covered rubber rings, for most of the wounded had to sit on them in bed, and every night rubbed down a dozen men with alcohol and powder. Of course there was a grandfather on our ward. One always called the older ones *grandpere* or *mon vieux*. Our grandfather was only thirty years old, though he had a beard and looked almost any age. He was nicknamed "The Tiger", and was certainly a rough customer. His arm and leg on one side were both badly wounded, and he had a hole in his forehead besides. A Carrel tube issued from his bandaged head, and I was obliged to squirt Dakin solution into it every two hours. He called the tube his telephone and used to tell me what he heard through it. We couldn't make out if he was a little out of his mind or very original and amusing.'

American nurse Ellen LaMotte also volunteered to serve close to the front lines in Europe. From the outset she was determined to work as a nurse and she satiated this ambition years before the United States entered the war. She started her nursing career as a tuberculosis nurse in Baltimore, Maryland. On arriving in Europe, she first went to the American Hospital at Neuilly, a French commune just west of Paris, only to discover to her chagrin that it already had more than enough volunteers. She was then introduced to Mary Borden, the daughter of a wealthy American businessman and the wife of an English merchant, who was running a field hospital in Belgium. LaMotte joined her and served in a French field hospital with the French Army from 1915 to 1916.

By 1915 she was in Belgium. Her 1916 book, *The Backwash of War*, was one of the first publications to present international audiences with first-hand views of the day-to-day horrors she witnessed. The book was considered so explicit at the time that it wasn't reprinted until 1934. In one chapter titled 'Locomotor ataxia', which means loss of coordination of movement, Ellen described her experiences:

'The seriously wounded were unloaded carefully and placed upon beds covered with rubber sheeting, and clean sacking, which protected the thin mattresses from blood. The patients were afterwards covered with red blankets, and stone hot water bottles were also given them, sometimes. But in the sorting tent there were no such comforts. They were not needed. The sick men and the slightly wounded could sit very well on the backless benches till the [Doctor in charge] had time to come and examine them.

'Quite a company of "sitters" were assembled here one morning, helped out of two big ambulances that drove in within ten minutes of each other. They were a dejected lot, and they stumbled into the tent unsteadily, groping towards the benches, upon which they tried to pose their weary, old, fevered bodies in comfortable attitudes. And as it couldn't be done, there was a continual shifting movement, and unrest. Heavy legs in heavy wet boots were shoved stiffly forward, then dragged back again. Old, thin bodies bent forward, twisted sideways, coarse, filthy hands hung supine between spread knees, and then again the hands would change, and support whiskered, discouraged faces. They were all uncouth, grotesque, dejected, and they smelt abominably, these *poilus* [hairy], these hairy, unkempt soldiers. At their feet, their sacks lay, bulging with their few possessions. They hadn't much, but all they had lay there, at their feet. Old brown canvas sacks, bulging, muddy, worn, worn-out, like their owners. Tied on the outside were water cans, and extra boots, and bayonets, and inside were socks and writing paper and photographs of ugly wives. Therefore the ungainly sacks were precious, and they hugged them with their tired feet, afraid that they might lose them.

'Then finally the major arrived, and began the business of sorting them. He was brisk and alert, and he called them one by one to stand before him. They shuffled up to his little table, wavering, deprecating, humble, and answered his brief impatient questions. And on the spot he made snap diagnoses, such as rheumatism, bronchitis, kicked by a horse, knocked down by dispatch rider, dysentery, and so on a paltry, stupid lot of ailments and minor accidents, demanding a few days' treatment. It was a dull service, this medical service, yet one had to be always on guard against contagion, so the service was a responsible one. There is much bronchitis in Flanders, in the trenches, because of the incessant Belgian rain. They are sick with it too, poor devils. So said the major to himself as he made his rounds.'

The advent of World War I saw spectacular advances in anaesthetics, aseptic surgery and bacteriology, as well as the growth of the civilian and military medical professions. When the war began in August 1914 Germany could call on the services of 33,031 doctors (most of them state employees), 80 per cent of whom were mobilized. By October 1915, the French Army had drafted 18,000 doctors. Around 11,000 British doctors were also called up. The Great War was the first major conflict (apart from the Russo-Japanese War) in which deaths from wounds exceeded those from illness. In the Boer War two-thirds of the British soldiers died from disease. In general, the Western Front was best-provisioned to deal with the wounded. This wasn't the case in other theatres because seven times as many Turkish troops died from disease as from wounds, and disease was the main cause of fatalities in East Africa.

The Allies in Macedonia lost many more men to malaria than to the enemy forces. Typhus afflicted a quarter of the Serbian Army in 1915 and was a prime reason for its collapse. During the bitter fighting on the Eastern Front over 5 million Russian soldiers were hospitalized on account of disease, mainly scurvy but also typhus, typhoid, cholera and dysentery. Despite the ravages of disease most of the infected survived, and over the war as a whole five times as many soldiers died from combat wounds as from sickness.

Most British troops were provided with clean water, baths and laundry facilities once they were out of the line. German troops were deloused in mobile '*gouseleums*' paid for by public subscription. Smallpox had ravaged the French Army in 1870, but had been virtually eradicated by 1914. In the BEF in 1914, 31 per cent of the wounded contracted tetanus, but by the end of the war infection rates were down to 0.1 per cent. Twenty per cent of the American troops who fought the Spanish in 1898 contracted typhoid, but very few did in 1917–18. Diseases ranging from syphilis to trench foot (a condition similar to frostbite caused by feet being constantly immersed in water) did not threaten the belligerent armies' fighting strength and efficiency. This was largely due to the rise of a professional medical corps before 1914, as well as new developments in preventive medicine, that these afflictions affected proportionately fewer than in previous wars, and most of those who did fall victim could return to active duty.

Still more remarkable was medicine's success in rehabilitating the wounded, and this more than anything else accounted for the armies' ability to keep fighting despite frequently appalling casualties. After the war, almost every village or town in Europe had its quota of wounded warriors, some begging on high streets, some just wandering around. One French textile worker described her village in the north of the country:

'The agricultural labourers came back as amputees, blind, gassed, or as "scar throats", as some were called because of their disfigured, crudely healed faces. We began to see more and more returning. What a crowd! What a rude shock at the railway station, where the wives went to meet their husbands, to find them like that – crippled, sick, despairing that they would be of no use anymore.

At first, we had the impression that all those returning had been injured. It wasn't until later that those who had escaped without a scratch returned. But, like their comrades, they were serious, sad, unsmiling, they spoke little. They had lived in hell for four years and wouldn't forget it.'

When the casualties of the Great War returned home many were psychologically damaged. They would rarely if ever relate their experiences. These silent ones were not the same men who had rallied to the various flags of belligerent nations in 1914 and in 1917. Their pain was deep, profound and in many cases enduring. Then there were the ones with horrific facial damage. Reconstructive surgery was still in its infancy so many were reduced to wearing prosthetic facial features, such as noses, eyes, chins and sometimes whole jaw bones. Estimates vary, but at least 12 per cent of all men wounded suffered from facial injuries, and roughly one-third of these were permanently disfigured. The road to recovery for these men was often fraught with terrible pain and anguish. French Nurse Henriette Remi related the story of how she visited an officer friend in the spring of 1918. The officer had in his charge someone who he described as 'a man with no face'. He told Henriette: 'He has only one leg, his right arm is covered by bandages. His mouth is completely distorted by an ugly scar, which descends below his chin. All that is left of his nose are two enormous nostrils, two black holes, which trap our gaze, and make us wonder for what this man has suffered? All that is left of his face are his eyes, covered by a veil; his eyes seem to see.'

These were the ones for whom the war never ended. Most wars rarely do.

CHAPTER THIRTEEN

ANOTHER WORLD WAR

The wonderful work done by those courageous nurses in World War I paved the way for nurses to enrol in even greater numbers when hostilities commenced in 1939. Throughout the 1930s the International Committee of the Red Cross had prevaricated over direct involvement in some of the pressing issues that it was confronted with, such as the internment of political prisoners and the persecution of the Jews, but it would still play a significant role in World War II.

During World War II, the effectiveness of combat medics and military personnel providing frontline trauma care increased significantly, thanks to medical innovations.

A German biochemist, Gerhard Johannes Paul Domagk (1895–1964), conducted intensive research into antibacterial chemicals, which resulted in the discovery of a new class of drugs that provided the first effective treatments for pneumonia, meningitis and other bacterial diseases. When Domagk published his findings in 1935, doctors discovered that one of his compounds called Prontosil reduced many bacterial infections. Subsequently, other researchers developed derivatives based on the Prontosil sulfonamide group. The resulting so-called sulpha drugs revolutionized medicine and became particularly popular during World War II.

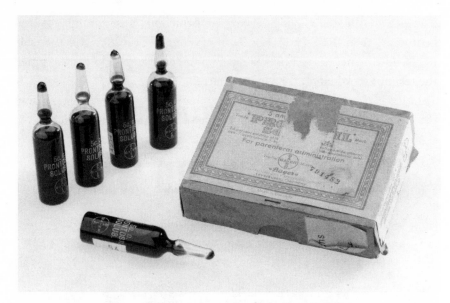

Prontosil was one of the earliest antimicrobial drugs used in World War II.

The discovery of sulphanilamide significantly reduced the mortality rate during World War II. Sulpha drugs were used routinely to control such diseases as pneumonia, gonorrhoea, meningitis, dysentery and streptococcal infections. American soldiers were taught to sprinkle sulpha powder immediately on any open wound to prevent infection. Every soldier was issued a first aid pouch that attached to their waist belt. The first aid pouch contained a package of sulpha powder and a bandage to dress the wound.

During World War I Scottish bacteriologist Sir Alexander Fleming (1881–1955) began experimenting with antibacterial substances, and in 1921 he discovered lysozyme, an antibiotic enzyme that attacks many types of bacteria. In 1928, he discovered the 'mould juice' secreted by something called penicillium. He immediately understood the potential medical value but it wasn't a done deal. Fleming had neither the resources nor the means to manufacture enough penicillin to be useful in practice; consequently, his discovery was dismissed as no more than a laboratory curiosity. A further ten years would pass before a team of scientists at Oxford University rediscovered Fleming's work. By this time, they had more convincing evidence of the remarkable powers of penicillin. The timing was bad because by then Britain was heavily involved in World War II and unable to provide the necessary funds to develop the drug further. This prompted the team to seek help in the United States.

In 1941 John Davenport and Gordon Cragwall, two representatives from the pharmaceutical company Pfizer, attended a symposium. During the symposium researchers from Columbia University presented irrefutable evidence that penicillin could effectively treat infections.

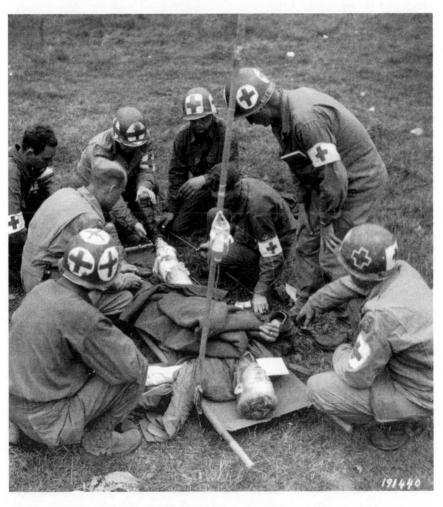

Combat medics at work during the Battle of Normandy, 1944.

The two men recognized the potential and promptly offered Pfizer's assistance. It would take another couple of years and involve many pitfalls before they could effectively mass-produce what became widely regarded as the world's first wonder drug. By June 1942, only enough penicillin had been produced to treat ten men. Army trials of the drug began in spring 1943 and were so successful that when Pfizer demonstrated that its scientists had found a deep-tank fermentation process to produce the drug, the government purchased 21 billion units. Eventually Pfizer produced 90 per cent of the penicillin that landed with the Allied forces at Normandy on D-Day in 1944, and more than half of all the penicillin used by the Allies for the remainder of the war. It helped to save countless lives. Penicillin remains one of the most active and safest antibacterials available. Further medical innovations such as blood plasma and whole blood also helped to reduce the fatality rate of battle casualties. World War II marked a watershed in the history of vaccine development as the military, in collaboration with academia and industry, achieved unprecedented levels of innovation in response to war-enhanced disease threats such as influenza and pneumococcal pneumonia. Wartime sponsored government programmes contributed to the development of new or significantly improved vaccines that tackled ten of the 28 vaccine-preventable diseases identified in the twentieth century.

In the United States, by 1943 the demand for trained nurses transcended previously accepted racial barriers. When the Cadet Nurse Corps was established in that year both black and white women, along with a few Native American women, entered the nursing profession. There were even a few Japanese-American internees in the programme. Over 115,000 Cadets were enrolled in both federal and non-federal hospitals. When General James Carre Magee was appointed surgeon general on 1 Jun 1939, he and his staff went on to play an integral part in the introduction of new drugs for military use and insisted on immunizing every soldier against typhoid and paratyphoid fevers, smallpox and tetanus, which kept the incidence of these diseases so low as to be almost insignificant. By the end of 1942, he had 30,000 doctors and 20,000 nurses serving the military.

World War II British nurses were known as the Queen Alexandra's Imperial Military Nursing Service (QAIMNS). Each QA had an officer status with equivalent rank but no actual commission status. This changed in 1941, when emergency commissions and rank structure were formulated to bring the QAs into line with the rest of the British Army. This meant that from 1941 onwards QAs wore rank badges, were eligible for promotion and received financial benefits along with ranks from lieutenant through to brigadier. From 1939 to 1945 members of the QAIMNS served in many countries ranging from Africa, Burma, China, Egypt, France, Gibraltar, Hong Kong, Iceland, Italy, Malaya, Malta, Normandy, Palestine and Singapore.

Nurse Dorothy Barre served in the US Army in World War II. She grew up on a farm on Millbury Road in Oxford, Massachusetts. Her grandfather, John Taft, had fought in the American Civil War and Dorothy was still a child when she moved to the centre of town to live with him. She graduated from Oxford High School in 1936, and then went to Simmons College before starting nurse's training at Massachusetts Memorial Hospital in Boston. She enlisted in the army on 5 July 1943, as a registered nurse, serial number N-752 051, and was stationed at Camp Edwards on Cape Cod before being assigned to the 16th General Hospital, which was reorganized at Fort Andrews, Massachusetts, on 1 September 1942. On 25 August 1943 the unit was moved to Fort Devens, where the nurses went through basic training.

On 21 December 1943 the unit was moved to Camp Miles Standish and one week later the 'hospital', with 100 nurses, 500 corpsmen and support staff, 60 male officers and four Red Cross volunteers, embarked on the transport ship *Edmund B. Alexander* from Boston. The ship arrived in Liverpool on 8 January 1944, and the 16th General Hospital set up at Oulton Park, Cheshire, before being moved to Penley Hall in Flintshire, Wales.

Eventually, in the summer of 1944 they shipped out to France, arriving on Utah Beach, Normandy, on 14 August – just a few weeks after D-Day. By 2 October the 16th General Hospital bivouaced in an area near Enghien les Bains, a few miles from Paris, where it remained until 9 October. Then it was relocated to Liege, in Belgium, in time for the Ardennes Offensive, also known as the Battle of the Bulge. Dorothy later recalled: 'I worked as a nurse in the surgical orthopaedic wards. We were set up in Liege before the Bulge broke, and we were in tents that would hold thirty patients at a time. In the centre of each tent was a potbelly stove that kept us warm, and we had surgical carts we could use for dressings. When the Bulge broke, Liege was an ammunition dump, so they were sending buzz bombs toward the city. We were in that alley of buzz bombs, and when we heard them, a patient would run out and see what route they were on. There were three routes that they fired over us. Over that period, we were hit three times with the buzz bombs, not where the patients were. We did not have any casualties. We were ten or twelve miles from the fighting. But one time one of the buzz bombs hit nearby, one of the houses, and we admitted Belgian patients. I had a mother and a daughter, and the daughter died. The doctor and I worked together to help them until they could get the mother to the Belgian hospital in Liege.

'Before the Bulge, we treated soldiers sometimes, but when the Bulge started, we got them from army trucks or stretchers. They might just be wrapped in blankets, the young fellas, and we got them washed up. Sometimes we would have four nurses to one guy, getting them washed up, pyjamas on, their dressings checked. We would ask them if they had pain, and we carried codeine and aspirin in our pockets. I remember sitting on the cots and talking with the guys. They would always ask me where I came from, since I have a Boston accent. Sometimes they would stay with us for just eight or ten hours. The patients would get a good meal and cleaned up and given penicillin too. After they were well enough, they were flown to Paris or London.'

All Allied soldiers in World War II received fairly frequent medical check-ups. Ensuring that a soldier was fit and healthy enough to perform their duties was just as important as tending the wounded. One soldier, Major Earl Edwards, was preparing to take 2nd Battalion, 22nd Infantry, 4th Infantry Division, ashore on D-Day 6 June. But before he could begin his assault into France Edwards had a certain problem he had to deal with. A few days before the actual landing he was suffering from a debilitating case of haemorrhoids that was causing him considerable discomfort. He found his ailment even affected his gait. He asked his roommate to report his condition to the colonel. He was sure his medical situation would prevent him from making the landings. In his memoirs Edwards described the events: 'Later in the day an ambulance drove up to our quarters and two medics came in and said that I was to come with them. They helped me to the ambulance where I found Col. Tribolet and the Regimental Surgeon, Dr. Kirtley. We drove away and soon parked in front of a U.S. Field Hospital. Col. Tribolet and Dr. Kirtley went in and soon returned. We then drove awhile and parked in front of another hospital.

'The same thing happened. So we drove on to another. This time some medics came out and carried me in and within a short time I was operated on. After an hour or so of recovery I was carried back to the ambulance, which returned me to my quarters, and I was placed again on my bunk. All this time no explanations whatever. I later learned that Col. Tribolet was determined that I would command the 2nd Battalion in the invasion so he and Doc Kirtley decided to take me to a hospital and ask if they would operate on me and immediately release me to their care. If the answer was "no" they simply carried me to another hospital and so on until one agreed.

'So I went into the landings with a large wad of cotton taped to my rear. Fortunately, the salt water and a few artillery rounds cured me. I don't remember ever thinking about it after we landed.'

The celebrated British comedian, writer and World War II veteran Spike Milligan served as a gunner with the Royal Artillery through the Tunis and Italian campaigns. He vividly described his harrowing experience of shell shock in his book *Mussolini: His Part in My Downfall*: 'Next I was at the bottom of the mountain, next I'm speaking to Major Jenkins, I am crying, I don't know why, he's saying, "Get that wound dressed." I said, "What wound?" I had been hit on the side of my right leg. "Why did you come back?" He is shouting at me and threatening me, I can't remember what I am saying. He's saying, "You could find your way back but you couldn't find your way to the OP." Next I'm sitting in an ambulance and shaking, an orderly puts a blanket round my shoulders, I'm crying again, why why why? Next I'm in a forward dressing station, an orderly gives me a bowl of hot very sweet tea, "Swallow these," he says, two small white pills. I can't hold the bowl for shaking, he takes it from me and helps me drink it.

'All around are wounded, he has rolled up my trouser leg. He's putting a sticking plaster on the wound, he's telling me it's only a small one. I don't really care if it's big or small, why am I crying? Why can't I stop? I'm getting lots of sympathy, what I want is an explanation. I'm feeling drowsy, and I must have started to sway because next I'm on a stretcher. I feel lovely, what were in those tablets … that's the stuff for me, who wants food? I don't know how long I'm there, I wake up. I'm still on the stretcher, I'm not drowsy, but I start to shiver. I sit up. They put a label on me. They get me to my feet and help me to an ambulance. I can see really badly wounded men, their bandages soaked through with blood, plasma is being dripped into them.'

Despite advances in psychiatry it appeared that in World War II the lessons of World War I had been largely ignored. There was still a stigma attached to those diagnosed with shell shock or combat fatigue. On 26 April 1943, General Omar N. Bradley issued a directive, which established a holding period of seven days for psychiatric patients at the 9th Evacuation Hospital, and for the first time the term 'exhaustion' was prescribed as the initial diagnosis for all combat psychiatric cases. Another reason 'exhaustion' was chosen was because it was considered to have no negative connotations that could attach it to the actual problem of neuropsychiatric disturbance. The implication being that psychiatric breakdown was the result of natural fatigue and that simple rest was sufficient to return men to duty. In World War II, combat stress casualties accounted for between 20 to 30 per cent of those wounded in action. In August 1943, Lieutenant General George S. Patton visited a hospital near Palermo. His well-publicized berating of a psychiatric casualty caused a media frenzy and a public outcry, but it also highlighted the issue of combat exhaustion and provided the necessary stimulus the military needed to deal with this debilitating condition.

Apart from a glaring lack of knowledge concerning psychiatric problems arising from exposure to combat, the US military had to deal with other pressing issues exacerbated by antiquated thinking. There was still racial segregation in the US armed forces at that time, and during World War II the US Army Nurse Corps was initially reluctant to accept black nurses into the service. Those that did join the service were only allowed to care for black troops in black wards or hospitals. In January 1941, the US Army established a quota of 56 black nurses for admission to the Army Nurse Corps. Through the efforts of the National Association of Colored

General Patton showed great respect to his wounded men but had less regard for those display-ing symptoms of battle fatigue.

Graduate Nurses (NACGN), the army quota was abolished before the end of the war and black women were able to serve with distinction in various capacities.

When the war ended in 1945 just 479 black nurses were serving in a corps of 50,000 because a quota system imposed by the segregated army during the first two years of the war restricted the number of black enrolments. By late July 1945, there were 512 black women in the Army's Nurse Corps, including nine captains and 115 first lieutenants. Of the three units that served overseas, one was a group of 63 black nurses who worked with the 168th Station Hospital in Manchester, England, caring for wounded German prisoners. In 1943, for example, the army limited the number of black nurses in the Nurse Corps to 160.

African-American nurses were not allowed to treat wounded white soldiers.

In December 1941, just a few days after the bombing of Pearl Harbor that initiated America's entry into World War II, a Detroit mother named Sylvia Tucker visited her local Red Cross donor centre to give blood. She had been inspired by the rousing appeals on national radio and wanted to do her part. When she arrived at the centre, the supervisor promptly turned her away and refused to accept her donation. Orders from the National Offices prohibited African-American blood donors at this time. Mrs Tucker was so shocked by the incident that she wrote an articulate and emotional letter of protest to first lady, Eleanor Roosevelt:

> 'I was shocked and grieved to learn that the "eternal color question" was paramount to the grave war situation. After explaining that both my loyalty to my country and to my young son, who will be eligible for Military Service in two months, prompted my offer, I challenged the doctor to accept my blood and place it in a container and label it "Negro Blood" and after due process make it available for some Negro mother's son, who, like his white American brothers-in-arms, must face shot and shell and death as these things know no "color line." … The American Red Cross holds the destiny of thousands of [humans], white and black, make them understand that "We are Americans, too".'

Charles R. Drew was an African-American physician who had developed ways to process and store blood plasma in 'blood banks' and conducted pioneering research on typing, preserving and storing blood for later transfusion. In 1941, he became the first African-American surgeon selected to serve as an examiner on the American Board of Surgery. He was later appointed director of the first American Red Cross Plasma Bank. Late in 1941, the surgeons general of the United States Army and Navy took the ignominious decision to inform the Red Cross that only blood from white donors would be accepted for military use. Despite the fact that it had been conclusively proven that there were no racial differences in blood, the military was conceding to prevailing social bias and substantial political pressure.

In January 1942, the War Department revised its position, agreeing to accept blood from black donors, but rigidly insisted on adherence to segregation of the blood supply. A black soldier could receive a blood transfusion from a Caucasian donor if there was nothing else available but the reverse wasn't possible. Surprisingly enough, the esteemed Red Cross not only accepted that decision but also declared that it had no interest in meddling with socio-racial controversies. Red Cross officials later offered that those who persisted in criticizing the policy were unpatriotically attempting to cripple the blood donor service and thus harm the war effort itself.

Drew openly denounced the policy, stating that there was absolutely no scientific evidence of any difference based on race, and declared that the racial segregation of blood was in contravention to scientific fact and an insult to patriotic black Americans. Because of this he was asked to resign from the Red Cross. He returned to Washington DC and became the head

An American soldier is given a blood transfusion in Sicily on 9 August 1943. It was against US army regulations to give African American blood to white soldiers.

of Howard University's Department of Surgery and later chief surgeon at the University's Freedman's Hospital. Drew died on 1 April 1950, in Burlington, North Carolina, from injuries sustained in a car accident while on his way to a conference at the Tuskegee Institute in Alabama. The government rescinded its policy on blood segregation eight months after Drew's death.

Della H. Raney, a graduate of the Lincoln Hospital School of Nursing in Durham, North Carolina, was the first African-American nurse to be commissioned as a lieutenant in the Army Nurse Corps during World War II. Her first tour of duty was at Fort Bragg, North Carolina. As a lieutenant serving at the famous Tuskegee Army Airfield in Alabama, she was appointed chief nurse, Army Nurse Corps, in 1942, effectively the first African-American to receive this appointment. She later served as chief nurse at Fort Huachuca, Arizona. Raney was promoted to captain in 1945. After the war, she was assigned to head the nursing staff at the station hospital at Camp Beale, California. In 1946, she was promoted to major and served a tour of duty in Japan. Major Raney retired in 1978.

The remarkable Mabel Staupers had championed Raney's cause. During World War II Staupers worked as the executive secretary of the National Association of Colored Graduate Nurses (NACGN), where she led the movement to gain full integration of black nurses into the armed forces and the professional nursing organizations. The purpose of the NACGN was to confront the marginalization of black nurses and to advance the standing and best interests of trained nurses. The organization accomplished higher standards of nursing and an overall shift in society by exposing the burdens of discrimination and segregation. The struggle to achieve recognition, status and acceptance of black nurses into the institutional structures of American nursing was significantly advanced because of her leadership.

Mabel Staupers was born in Barbados on 27 February 1890. In April 1903, her family migrated to the United States and in September of that year settled in Harlem, New York. She was admitted to the Freedmen's Hospital School of Nursing in 1914, graduating with honours in 1917. That same year she married Dr James Max Keaton of Asheville, North

Carolina. This marriage ended in divorce, and in 1931 she married Frisby Staupers, of New York City.

Her professional career began with private duty nursing in New York City and Washington DC. In 1920, in cooperation with the late Dr Louis T. Wright and Dr James Wilson, she organized the Booker T. Washington Sanatorium, the first facility in the Harlem area where Negro doctors could treat their patients. She served this institution as administrator and director of nurses. In 1921 she was awarded a working fellowship to the Henry Phipps Institute for Tuberculosis in Philadelphia, Pennsylvania. She was later assigned to the chest department of the Jefferson Hospital Medical College in Philadelphia. Her experience there with the segregation and discrimination of staff and patients was one of the motivating forces which made her in later years, in cooperation with Dr Wright, work for full and equal opportunities in all health programmes and services in America. She strove for the inclusion of black nurses to the army and navy during World War II. African-American nurses had shown interest in joining the Army Nurse Corps as early as 1927, but to no avail. When a black nurse applied for admission to the corps in late September 1940, she was told in no uncertain terms that army regulations made no provision for the appointment of 'negro nurses'. In 1940, when approached on the subject of using black nurses, the surgeon general of the US Army Medical Corps, James C. Magee, had been non-committal in his response. Part of his reply ran as follows: 'Their employment has been found impracticable in time of peace. You may rest assured that when military conditions make it practicable for the war department to use colored nurses they will not be overlooked.'

The American Red Cross, the National Association of Colored Graduate Nurses and other nursing organizations protested the army's policy of excluding African-American nurses. When Mabel Staupers confronted President Franklin Roosevelt on the issue he responded by reassuring her that the War Department was considering the employment of black nurses. By April 1941 there were 48 black nurses assigned to Camp Livingston, Louisiana, and in Fort Bragg, North Carolina. The number of black nurses had tripled by May 1943.

During World War II, African-American nurses served in all theatres of the war including Africa, Burma, Australia and England. The first black medical unit to deploy overseas was the 25th Station Hospital Unit, which contained 30 nurses. The unit went to Liberia in 1943 to care for US troops protecting strategic airfields and rubber plantations. The nurses wore helmets and carried full packs containing gas masks and canteen belts. The Red Cross arm bands and lack of weapons distinguished them from those who were actually fighting troops. Mabel Staupers continued to fight for the full inclusion of nurses of all races and this was finally granted in 1945. By the end of World War II, approximately 600 African-American nurses had served their country, and by 1948 the American Nursing Association allowed them to join their ranks.

Female army nurses who served in combat areas during World War II were a vital element of the health provision combatants received, but despite their massive contribution they remained largely unrecognized for their service. One particular black woman who volunteered to serve with a US Army medical unit remained anonymous for over 65 years.

War and conflict can produce the most unlikely heroes and heroines. Augusta Chiwy was one. She died on 23 July 2015 at the grand old age of 94 in a geriatric care home on the outskirts of Brussels and was buried in Bastogne with full military honours. Her character appeared all too briefly in the famed *Band of Brothers* TV series, where she was portrayed as 'Anna from the Congo' in the 'Bastogne' episode.

Augusta's story is quintessentially about two people, a doctor and a nurse whose paths would never have crossed had it not been for the siege of Bastogne. They had a relationship that left no time for romantic interludes. They were too preoccupied trying to save lives and care for wounded soldiers with little more than bandages and antiseptic powder, performing surgery with no surgical instruments and using only Cognac for anaesthesia.

In 1930, at the tender age of nine, Augusta was brought to Bastogne in Belgium by her white European father, a travelling veterinarian called Henry Chiwy. Her mother was Congolese, and Augusta was one of many mixed-race children resettled in Belgium from the Congo, which at that time was a Belgian colony. After growing up in Bastogne, Augusta left for the northern Flemish town of Leuven in her early twenties to attend nursing school. She remained in Leuven after graduating and worked at the St Elizabeth Hospital, which was staffed by the Augustine Congregation Sisters. In December 1944 she accepted an invitation from her father to return to Bastogne and spend Christmas with him and his sister-in-law (whom she called 'Mama Caroline').

Augusta's timing could not have been worse. Although the Allies had made major territorial gains in Belgium and France after D-Day in their push towards Berlin, by December 1944 the Germans were about to fight back – and their focus of their counter-offensive was the Belgian Ardennes, one of whose key strategic towns was Bastogne. Just as Augusta arrived home, the Battle of the Bulge began.

Her festive plans put to one side, Augusta found herself volunteering to work with the 10th Armored Division and then the 101st Airborne. Many, many Americans survived this epic encounter because of her. After World War II Augusta didn't return to full-time nursing until 1967. The reason why was that Augusta was stricken by a form of PTSD known as selective mutism. Any mention of the war or Bastogne would make her clam up completely.

The surgeon at the 20th AIB Aid Station in Bastogne where Augusta worked was Dr John 'Jack' Prior, who hailed from a small town in Vermont. Jack and Augusta weren't just from different countries with different languages, they were from different worlds. It was the fortunes of war that brought them together and tore them apart. But in the few weeks that they worked side by side in the army hospitals they forged a deep bond that endured for decades after the war.

On the morning of 16 December 1944 Augusta left Leuven by tram, but when she reached Brussels to transfer southward she discovered that all trains bound for Bastogne and Luxembourg were terminating at the city of Namur. From there passengers were loaded onto cattle trucks, the only form of transportation available, and taken to the town of Marche. It was a chilly ride, with temperatures plunging to minus 20 and worse. December 1944 was the coldest winter in northern Europe in living memory. After spending more than 15 hours on the road and having used trains, trucks, a US Army Willys Jeep and even a bicycle, she finally reached Bastogne at around 11.00 pm that evening.

Born in the Belgian Congo and brought to Belgium at the age of nine, nurse Augusta Chiwy demonstrated remarkable skill, compassion and courage that saved many American lives during the devastating Battle of the Bulge in December 1944.

The town of Bastogne was no stranger to conflict. A group of devoutly religious nuns known as The Sisters of Notre Dame began preparing the town's cellars as places of refuge, just as they had done in 1940. As worried Bastogne civilians began to flock there, Augusta volunteered to assist. She was completely oblivious to the fact that three German armies had broken through the lightly defended Western Front in an all-out effort to seize the port of Antwerp, with the intent of dividing the Allies and ending the war. As they advanced westward, leaving a trail of destruction in their wake, a significant 'bulge' in the Allied battle lines began to take shape that gave this battle its name. As the situation grew more desperate, the 10th Armored rushed three teams comprising 2,700 men to Bastogne. Among them was army doctor (Captain) Jack Prior, who found himself just north of Bastogne in the village of Noville attempting to hold back the enemy onslaught. Dense Ardennes mist exacerbated an already desperate situation, and after little less than 48 hours the diminutive force was overwhelmed and evacuated to Bastogne.

A few days later the strategically important market town of Bastogne became completely surrounded by enemy forces. Having lost a number of his men in Noville, Jack instructed his second in command, Captain Irving Lee Naftulin, to comb the market town for anyone with medical experience to aid their efforts. Naftulin found two people – a young nurse named Renée Lemaire and Augusta Chiwy. Both women agreed to join forces with Jack to prepare and treat the steadily increasing number of casualties as US forces struggled to maintain their tenuous hold on the city against repeated onslaughts by well-equipped German divisions. As German artillery fire began to intermittently fall inside the American perimeter, the small group set up shop in a recently abandoned building that had served as a grocery store. With living quarters upstairs and a cellar below, it was about the best location available for a new aid station.

Jack discovered that Augusta was incredibly adept at dealing with the bloodiest and most grave of injuries, handling amputees, bleeding, large thoracic wounds and other results of battlefield trauma. Renée was the comforter, best at soothing soldiers in pain and keeping them clean. Because racism was still fairly institutionalized in the United States in 1944, Augusta, as a mixed-race woman, was the subject of bigotry on more than a few occasions. There were many American soldiers who refused to be treated by her, to which Jack's response was usually: 'She treats you, or you die.' Augusta quickly discovered that death is a great leveller.

On a few occasions, Jack and Augusta made extremely risky trips to the front lines to evacuate the wounded. One of the most significant of these was at a promontory just outside Bastogne called Mardasson Hill, which today is the location of the largest American monument outside the United States. Here, Augusta and Jack came under intense rifle, machine gun and artillery fire in a dangerously exposed position. Despite this, they still managed to treat and evacuate several critically wounded men. Augusta, who wore a long nurse's gabardine, came through unscathed, but discovered several bullet holes in the garment. In later years, Augusta recalled in interviews that Jack had remarked: 'Looks like they almost got you. It's a good thing you're small.' She retorted that, 'A black face in all this snow is an easy target. The Germans are just bad shots.'

As the Nazi vice tightened its grip on Bastogne, casualties mounted considerably. And due to the intense, all-pervading mist the air forces were unable to re-supply the besieged garrison until 23 December. Up until that point Jack's medics were forced to use bed sheets and any other available fabric as bandages. In one extreme case, Jack and Augusta amputated one man's hand and leg using nothing more than the serrated edge of an army-issue survival knife and anaesthesia provided by a bottle of requisitioned Five Star Cognac.

On Christmas Eve, Jack and Augusta briefly left the aid station to enjoy a glass of champagne provided by a resourceful GI in the adjacent house. Once inside, they heard the unmistakable drone of approaching aircraft. But what they thought was another airdrop was in fact an enemy bombing mission. Their aid station took a direct hit from a 225 kg (500 lb) bomb. The percussion threw Jack to the ground and blew Augusta clean through a brick wall. Miraculously, they both emerged relatively unscathed, but their aid station was levelled and 30 patients inside were killed, along with Renée Lemaire, whose fragile body was blown into two pieces. The following day Jack reported for duty at the 101st Airborne HQ at the Heintz barracks, and Augusta followed him.

They continued to work together almost ceaselessly, day and night. They saved lives together and watched life slip away together. And on more than one occasion they barely escaped death together. Bastogne was liberated by General George Patton's 3rd Army on 26 December, and on 17 January Jack and Augusta were forced to say their goodbyes. They wouldn't see each other again until more than five decades later. Their story is one of incredible bravery, compassion and devotion. It's a tale of tenderness in the midst of appalling inhumanity enriched with a depth of caring that went mostly unexpressed and unacknowledged.

Jack returned home in 1945, became a respected pathologist and raised a family. Augusta also survived to raise a family, but suffered severe PTSD for the rest of her life. In 1948, the Red Cross sent her a desultory letter of thanks for her service, but her incredible efforts were largely forgotten after the war and she had absolutely no desire to recount them. After a fervent campaign to get Augusta the recognition she so richly deserved was launched in 2011, the Belgian king Albert II officially declared her a Knight of the Order of the Crown, which is basically the equivalent of a knighthood. Then the 101st Airborne Division presented her with the Civilian Humanitarian Medal. Augusta had finally received her just acknowledgement.

Isabelle Cook had just graduated from Mount Sinai Hospital School of Nursing when the war broke out. Unbeknown to her family, she volunteered to go oversees with the Army Nurse Corps. On 5 May 1943, Isabelle and her colleagues arrived in Casablanca, Morocco, and spent three months waiting for the Germans to be defeated in Tunisia. Over the next three years, the 3rd General Hospital in which she served would follow the front into Italy and then France. Cook celebrated the end of the war by marching in the VE Day parade in Aix-en-Provence, France, alongside Allied soldiers. Shortly thereafter, the order came to close down the 3rd General in August 1945 and Isabelle received her formal discharge in December 1945, having earned the rank of first lieutenant.

She wrote a book about her experiences titled *In times of war*. The following abridged interview was made for the Library of Congress Veterans' History Project:

> 'We spent about three months in Casablanca because of the fact that the Germans were still fighting in Tunisia and our hospital, the thousand-bed general hospital, was supposed to be set up in Mateur. That was just outside of Tunis. When the Germans were defeated in North Africa, then we got our orders to proceed to Mateur in Tunisia. I was one of the ten nurses that was chosen to

go on the advance party. We travelled 1,500 miles across country, across North Africa in a two-and-a-half-ton truck, an open truck and the heat was … unbearable. But we managed to go across... [and] we took over the French Army barracks that were used as a hospital by the Germans.

'In fact, there were still German prisoners, well they were German soldiers that were so severely wounded they could not be evacuated. They left one German doctor to care for them. So they immediately became prisoners of war. So we took care of them. There were German signs all over the place. Well, the rest of our unit arrived about several days later. They had had a terrible experience going cross-country in … cattle cars and even one of our nurses had died as a result of heat...

'Well, we set up our entire hospital in about eight days, 800 tons of equipment, generators, we had our own portable generators and the whole hospital was set up and the nurses and the nursing personnel had tents. There were five of us in each tent and outside latrines and outside wash stations and things like that. The heat … we were getting the winds, the "taraka" winds from the Sahara and living in the tents, it was pretty bad. But we were taking care of the casualties from Sicily. The Sicilian campaign had started and within about five days after we set up the hospital, we started receiving patients.

'They were evacuated by air and we acted as an evacuation hospital instead of a general hospital which takes care of the more severely wounded and those that needed to stay much longer. But we received about 2,000 patients. And as a result, we had to open another thousand-bed hospital … the field in tents and those that were convalescent moved into the tent area and the more seriously injured were in the building. We all did double shifts because we had to care for all these patients. And the heat was so unbearable and for the patients in the tents … we stayed in North Africa for one year and we took care of about 5,000 patients during that time....

'Since there was not very much action after VE Day, we were so short I worked in the orthopaedic section taking care of orthopaedic patients, but in Italy, they were so short of nurse anaesthetists that they decided to train two nurses to become anaesthetists, you know, just on-the-job training.

'We had a major who was an anaesthesiologist and he took over the job of teaching us anaesthesia. So they chose myself and one other, you know, another friend of mine, to become nurse anaesthetists. We… were doing that for the last year and a half that I was in the Service.'

World War II was the catalyst for many innovations in the treatment of battlefield trauma wounds. It also led to the transformation of the pharmaceutical industry, the development of the modern air transportation system, the introduction of the helicopter and major advances in the medical field of psychiatry. This was also the war that saw the advent and use of the most terrifying, devastating weapon ever developed by mankind, the atomic bomb, which was first used against Japan in August 1945.

American Army nurse Ruth Hass had been working with her unit in the Philippines, caring for US and Filipino soldiers, and then treating American POWs liberated from Japanese captivity. At that time they were building up medical teams to cope with the eventual expected invasion of Japan. When World War II ended with the formal surrender of Japan in September 1945, Ruth was with a group of army nurses stationed overseas waiting for an assignment. Two months later, in November 1945, she was airlifted to Kure, a major naval base. One day, they got an opportunity to relieve the boredom and do a little impromptu sightseeing, but they didn't expect to see the sheer scale of destruction caused by the atomic bomb that had been dropped on Hiroshima.

World War II casualties, both military and civilian, were completely unprecedented. No previous war in history had experienced more people killed or more property destroyed. After eight years of war in the Far East, six years of fighting in Europe, the largest war in human history was finally over. Although statistics are often contradictory, and even today it is still difficult to say precisely how many people perished during the war, the final tally in human life is currently estimated at 7.5 million Soviet troops, 3.5 million Germans, 1.25 million Japanese, 452,000 British and Commonwealth and around 295,000 American service personnel. Exact figures for other Allied armies vary. Civilian deaths exceeded military. At least 19 million Soviet civilians, 10 million Chinese and 6 million European Jews lost their lives during the war.

The end of World War II would directly and indirectly shape world history for the next five decades. This period was known as the post-war era and was dominated by what became known as the Cold War. It was also dominated by fervent anti-communist sentiment spurred on by fanatics such as Senator Joseph McCarthy and bodies such as the USA's House Un-American Activities Committee. One of the major events that occurred as a direct consequence of World War II was the Korean War that broke out in 1950 after the partition of that country.

CHAPTER FOURTEEN

KOREA AND THE REAL MASH

It is frequently referred to as the 'Forgotten War', but for those who found themselves embroiled in this bitter conflict it will never be forgotten. The actions that occurred in the Korean peninsula between 1950 and 1953 were in many ways comparable to anything that happened in World War II. It was the war that ended with a fragile armistice, the consequences of which still resonate today in the tensions between the two Koreas, one a democracy and economic powerhouse, the other a brutally repressive dictatorship ruling over a poverty-stricken populace.

In 1904, Japan invaded Korea and made the country a protectorate, effectively making it a colony. When Japan's empire collapsed at the end of World War II, the Korean peninsula was in 1948 divided into two nations, North and South Korea, with North Korea falling under the Soviet Union sphere of influence and South Korea reliant on the USA for support and survival. The border between the two countries, known as the 38th Parallel, became one of the most dangerous places on Earth, where the proxies of the USSR and the USA faced each other in an uneasy stand-off that, on more than one occasion, threatened to break out into full-scale conflict. It was one of the leading candidates worldwide where the Cold War was most likely to turn into a hot war.

By 1949, the Russians had withdrawn their forces from the peninsula. But this was not a prelude to peace. Far from it. No sooner had the

Russians left than their North Korean allies launched an all-out attack across the border into the South on 25 June 1950 in an attempt to unify the peninsula under a communist regime. In response, the United Nations Security Council approved a resolution put forward by the United States calling for an armed force to repel the North Korean invaders. The Korean War had begun. By this time, major advances in military medicine and battlefield health care had been developed – not least in the form of Mobile Army Surgical Hospital (MASH) units. Their purpose was to provide the wounded with surgical care at as close a proximity as was reasonably possible to the battlefront. They were instigated because of experiences in World War II that proved wounded personnel suffered if there was a delay in providing definitive treatment of their injuries. This was the first war where helicopters were regularly used as flying ambulances to transport the injured to better-provisioned medical facilities in the shortest time possible. Ground-breaking new techniques such as plastic utility bags and the national blood-banking programme saved countless lives. Effective body armour was developed to allow better mobility while offering protection. These radical improvements not only saved the lives of soldiers in combat, they were soon adopted by the civilian sector.

Dr Elliott Cutler, soon to be appointed brigadier general and consultant to the surgeon general said, 'I would even urge an extension of this forward surgery, believing surgery should be brought to the soldier, not the soldier to the surgeon.' The MASH units were a new kind of organization that had been announced on 23 August 1945. It looked good on paper, but when the Korean War broke out these units were woefully unprepared. There were only 156 Medical Corps officers in the US 8th Army for example, while 346 was the authorized strength. It was immediately necessary to staff the 8054th evacuation hospital and the 8055th, 8063rd and 8076th MASHs. Reserves were mobilized and in June of 1950, owing to a shortage of doctors in the US Army Medical Corps, the government instituted a 'doctor draft'. At that time very few US military medical units had any experience in northeast Asia. Colonel Chauncey Dovell, 8th US Army surgeon, quickly dispatched MASH units to Korea to provide medical support. Consequently, eight MASH units were able to deploy rapidly and it didn't take them long to adapt to the rugged terrain on the peninsula.

The working practices of the ubiquitous MASH units during the Korean War were not that far removed from the popular 1970s American TV series. The characters of Hawkeye and Major 'Hot Lips' Houlihan were based on real people.

One of the doctors called up during the draft was Robert L. Emanuele. He later recalled:

> 'I was one of them, just a few years out of medical school with little surgical training and certainly no experience with "battlefield medicine". The thought of going to Korea scared me to death. It wasn't so much that I feared getting injured or even killed, but what really worried me was that I might not be a good enough doctor to provide the lifesaving skills that our soldiers would need. After a few weeks of training at Camp Atterbury in Indiana, I was sent to Korea, assigned as a surgeon with the 8209th MASH Unit. I arrived at the unit the morning of Sept. 22, 1951. MASH units were designed to

be mobile and operate close to the battlefield, and the 8209th was about 10 miles from the front when I arrived. I remember hearing the sounds of artillery shells in the distance and thinking "Wow, this really is happening." I don't recall much of that first day, but I do remember being cold and homesick my first night. One of the nurses brought me a sweater and blanket. The blanket was from Marshall Field & Co. Strange what you remember.'

The medical work
'Almost every day there was work to do. It would always start with the announcement over the camp's public address system of "incoming wounded". This was quickly followed by the sound of "choppers" coming in. I recall our unit had four helicopters. There were many examples of heroic acts in Korea, but the helicopter pilots were heroic on every flight. They would pluck wounded soldiers from the battlefield, sometimes under heavy fire. I was always amazed how brave those pilots were.

'The workdays were long, 12 hours on and 12 hours off, and the work was a constant challenge in terms of the sheer volume of cases and in the complexity and variety of wounds. Out of necessity, we often operated solo, with the assistance of a nurse or medical technician.

'The wounds could be horrific. A common injury was the result of an anti-personnel mine known as the "Bouncing Betty". When tripped, it fired straight up about three feet before it exploded, usually disembowelling or maiming those unfortunate enough to be within range. It was a horrible weapon. A lot of the surgery we did was on the lower extremity, doing our best to repair eviscerated abdomens and slaughtered lower limbs.

'The work was also emotionally challenging. I remember one particular case where a young soldier had been badly injured. Myself, Ray [Capt. Ray Crissy] and Mert [Maj. Merton White] worked on him for hours. We had opened his chest when his heart just stopped beating. We did everything we could to keep him alive, including injecting blood directly into his aorta and massaging his heart. I still remember the feeling of holding his heart in my hand. We were able to bring him back and I remember joking with him a few days later. He seemed to be doing well and I really thought he was going to make it. But his kidneys ultimately failed and we lost him. Like so many of the GIs, he was a nice kid whose life ended way too early.'

In the 1970s, the story of the fictional 4077th MASH unit caught the attention of Hollywood that resulted in an iconic movie, that went on to become a hit TV series, which ran for 11 seasons and actually lasted much longer than the conflict it portrayed. Although many agree that Robert Altman's 1970 movie *M*A*S*H* was ostensibly about the Vietnam War, it was based on the 1968 book *M*A*S*H*, a novel about three army doctors by Richard Hooker, assisted by sports writer Wilfred C. Heinz. All of the later *M*A*S*H* books written from 1974 through to 1997 were co-authored by William E. Butterworth (military novelist W.E.B. Griffin). Richard Hooker was a pseudonym. His real name was H. Richard Hornberger from Bremen, Maine, and he based his fictional books on his real-life experiences as a doctor at the 8055th MASH in Korea.

The 8055th ran a 60-bed hospital and was the first medical unit to arrive in Korea, in Busan, on 6 July 1950. Hornberger claimed that Hawkeye Pierce, the story's main character, was based on himself. Many claim that one of the nurses who inspired the character of 'Hotlips' Houlihan was based on Captain Ruth Dickson, chief nurse of the 8055th. Another possible contender was 'Hotlips' Hammerly, said to be a very attractive blonde from El Paso, Texas. Both were career army nurses who achieved high ranks.

Hollywood actor Jamie Farr, who played the cross-dressing Corporal Klinger, whose only ambition was to get a Section 8 discharge, wasn't the only member of the cast who actually served in Korea, albeit a few years after the war had ended. Alan Alda joined the Army Reserve after graduating from Fordham University in 1956 and completed a minimum six-month tour of duty as a gunnery officer in Korea. Although some websites erroneously claim he participated in the war, he was only 14 when it broke out.

The spark that caused Hornberger to begin writing about the war was a visit he received in the mid-1960s from a couple of old comrades who had served with him in the 8055th MASH, physician Dale Drake and his wife, Cathy. They spent some time reminiscing about their old experiences and Hornberger was inspired to begin writing down those memories.

Cathy (neé McDonough) Drake first arrived in Korea in 1950 as part of the Army Nurse Corps at the 8076th MASH before the unit was dispatched to Pyongyang, in North Korea. She was later assigned back to South Korea, when she went to work for the 8055th MASH unit, right on the 38th Parallel, where she met her future husband, Dale. She remembered: 'I was an army nurse stationed in Walter Reed Hospital in Washington, D.C., and I got assigned to the 171st Evacuation Hospital in Korea. I went from Fort Bragg to California, and then we sailed to Tokyo. The 171st Evac was a big hospital, and I was sent over to one of the five MASH units they had in Korea. That's where one of the doctors, an anaesthesiologist, was waiting for his replacement to come, and he told me "Now that would be a nice guy for you, Cathy".'

The anaesthesiologist was referring to Dale. While Dale was working as a chief anaesthesiologist in Arkansas he had joined the Army Reserve and in 1951 he was issued with orders to join the Far East Command, whereupon he was assigned to the 8055th.

Another Korean War medic was James O. Stapleton, who served with the Army Medical Corps. He enlisted in the army in 1948 at Ann Arbor, Michigan. From there he took his basic training and eventually wound up in Osaka, Japan, with the 25th Division, Medical Corps. President Truman gave some of these men the option to return to the US. James had been offered another stripe but had plans to return home to resume his education and go back to college. That never happened. As he later recalled: 'Now, this was in January of 1951 and it took them probably, oh, five or six days just to locate this group and I wound up in the mortar platoon as their medic. They had lost two medics, and so that's how we were replacements. And what we would do, we would go on patrol and I was the medic. And just a little side-line, I never knew where to wind up in that line when we were on patrol, whether it'd be safer to be up front, in the middle, or the back, so I'd try to alternate where I was and one of the things that I kind of

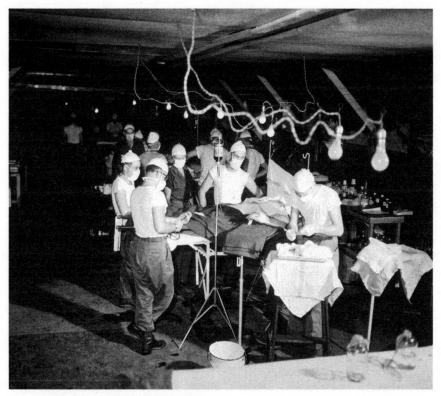

Surgery taking place at the 8209th MASH unit.

thought was rather unusual was the fact that there were so many different weapons. We had sub-machine guns. In fact, I had to carry an M1 until I was lucky enough to get a carbine, which was a lighter weight, because I had all the medical equipment with me. But I'll tell you one thing I did see on my first patrol. We were going along and here was a helmet and it had a red cross with a bullet hole right through that red cross. So, of course that was a no-no anymore. You didn't wear a red cross on your hat. I got an idea that this could be dangerous out here. But we went on a lot of patrols and were so mobile that we would get information that there was some people over in the next mountain or far down the road and we would jump in our trucks and vehicles and head there just as fast as we could to intercept them.

'The Clearing Company in the Medical Corps in the Army, was about three to four miles behind the line. Ambulances brought people to us. Now, they, wounded, once on the helicopter would go to a MASH unit, maybe ten miles back or further, and that was a very funny series, the MASH series on TV; but I bet you that there was never a MASH unit that was ever attacked by anybody because they were too far behind the line, but this Clearing Company, though, that I was in, we did a lot of work for people. And the thing that bothered me more than anything when I was over there was children stepping on land mines, having to work on them. You know, if you got a GI, that's, that's what's going to happen most likely. If you're going to get wounded, you're going to get shot; but for a child, just not knowing and, those darn French, they would put out land mines and they might clear a path through them but they never knew where the rest of them were and they would just leave them. And so, these civilians would get out there and they were just kids and some of the grown-ups, too, would lose their limbs.'

The Korean War was a tragic, fratricidal conflict that inflicted corrosive and lasting wounds on the peninsula. It can be correctly regarded in retrospect as one of the most destructive wars of the twentieth century. It is estimated that as many as three million Koreans died, at least half of them civilians. It was the war that established the American base structure abroad and a national security state at home, as defence spending nearly quadrupled in the last six months of 1950. While South Korea adopted democracy and capitalism, North Korea remains today one of the most extreme and isolated communist states in the world. The Korean War is most definitely not forgotten.

CHAPTER FIFTEEN

MEDS IN VIETNAM

Throughout the 1960s and on into the 70s, the Vietnam conflict was beamed into living rooms around the world. For those who remember, it was like watching a surreal war movie, with the exception being that this was the real thing and those were real lives. Some of the most prolific and unambiguous images were of casualties being airlifted in Huey Bell helicopters, accompanied by the soundtrack of whirring blades and small arms popping in all directions. For the young Americans who were drafted it wasn't about the political machinations of corrupt governments or polarized ideologies, their service hinged on one pervasive question: Am I going to make it out of here? For those who were wounded, whether they would make it out or not depended on two primal factors: the severity of the wound and the effectiveness of the medical treatment they received.

On the whole, medical supply support for the US Army in Vietnam was excellent considering the many problems and hindrances it initially encountered. In 1965, for instance, some operational US units in the field were experiencing supply problems. There were shortages across the board, especially for repair parts, munitions and even boots, clothing and organizational equipment. Part of the difficulty was that some materiel took longer to arrive than expected. Delays in receiving medical supplies meant that for several consecutive weeks soldiers who went down with anything more serious than heat rash or diarrhoea had to be evacuated to the 8th Field Hospital at Nha Trang. It was easy to reproach the US Army on many levels, but when it came to the medical services they were second to none in Vietnam.

With this new conflict new methods had to be devised to deal with new kinds of battlefield trauma, such as those inflicted by mines, high velocity missiles and booby traps. The terrain didn't make things any easier either. Many wounded soldiers had to be extracted from jungles and paddy fields, or along waterways where human and animal excreta exacerbated the chances of infection. Helicopters were usually available to evacuate casualties to medical facilities before the condition of the seriously wounded deteriorated beyond help. Many factors contributed to the low mortality rate of casualties, such as rapid evacuation, the availability of whole blood, well established forward hospitals, advanced surgical techniques and improved medical management. Blood packaged in Styrofoam containers,

A US soldier is treated on the battlefield after a Vietcong attack in February 1968.

which allowed storage between 48 and 72 hours in the field, could be placed in the forward area in anticipation of casualties. Most forward hospitals in Vietnam even had air conditioning to neutralize the extreme heat, dust and humidity, and allow the use of state-of-the-art medical equipment.

The nature of the conflict in Vietnam demanded a different approach entirely from the medical services. There was no actual front as there had been in World War II and Korea. Consequently, soldiers in Vietnam saw more action than the US soldiers of all preceding wars combined. For instance, the average infantryman in the South Pacific during World War II experienced around 40 days of combat in four years. The average infantryman in Vietnam saw about 240 days of combat in one year thanks to the mobility of the helicopter.

There were no secure road networks in almost all of the combat areas, therefore helicopter evacuation was imperative to deal with the situation. Approximately 12,000 helicopters saw action in Vietnam and it's estimated that 40,000 pilots served in the war. Of the 2.29 million US military who served in Vietnam, more than one in ten became a casualty in some way or another. In total, 58,169 were killed and 304,000 were wounded. Although the percentage of dead is similar to other wars, amputations or crippling wounds were 300 per cent higher than in World War II.

The process of extracting the wounded by helicopter from battlefields became almost routine. All US Army hospitals in Vietnam, including the MUST (Medical Unit, Self-contained, Transportable) units, were established as permanent installations with area support missions. These military hospitals were usually attached or in close proximity to the numerous base camps that were dotted about the country and were regarded as relatively secure unless the base was under attack. MedEvac helicopters flew nearly 500,000 missions in Vietnam, airlifting 900,000 patients (of whom almost half were Americans). The average time lapse between being wounded and reaching a hospital was usually less than one hour and, as a result, less than 1 per cent of the casualties died of their wounds within the first 24 hours. This was mainly because of the talents of MedEvac physicians who opened surgical airways, performed thoracic needle decompressions and shock resuscitations en route to the allocated destination.

Between January 1965 and December 1970, 133,447 wounded were admitted to medical treatment facilities in Vietnam; 97,659 of these were admitted to hospitals. Apart from the MedEvac helicopters, the US military had five separate companies and five detachments of ground ambulances at their disposal. However, the primary purpose for these vehicles was transporting casualties from the landing zone, or LZ, to the hospital facility. Sometimes they were used to transport patients to other hospitals, but this depended largely on how secure the chosen route was at the time.

Despite the effectiveness of MedEvac helicopters in Vietnam, they were frequently beset by the problem of finding suitable landing zones in proximity to the action. In the jungle and on steep terrain it was often impossible to land the helicopter, therefore in many cases the wounded had to be moved to the nearest accessible site, but this entailed using personnel

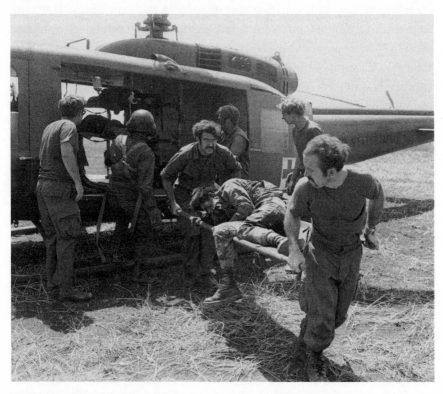

The Huey Bell Medevac helicopters were highly effective but often had problems in getting close to the action due to the nature of the terrain in Vietnam.

to physically carry the wounded from A to B. This only served to extend the waiting time and discomfort of the casualties. The solution to this problem was the Personnel Rescue Hoist, which was developed and improved to a reliable model by mid-1966.

Once the UH-1 helicopter was equipped with the necessary electrical system, the aircraft crew could quickly install or remove the hoist as required. The hoist itself consisted of a winch and cable on a boom that was extended out from the aircraft when it arrived over the rescue site. It was anchored to the floor and roof of the helicopter cabin, usually just inside the right-side door behind the pilot's seat. When the door was open, the hoist could be rotated on its support to position the cable and pulleys outside the aircraft, clear of the skids, so that the cable could be lowered to and raised from the ground. At the end of the cable was a ring and hook to which a Stokes litter or a rigid litter could be attached. The cable could be lowered at the rate of 45 m (150 ft) per minute and retracted at the rate of 36 m (120 ft) per minute. A slight variation on the theme was the forest penetrator, a spring-loaded device that could penetrate dense foliage, and opened to provide seats on which a casualty could be securely strapped in. This hoist was the preferred choice of the crews over the litter version because it was less likely to become entangled in the trees and foliage.

On a hoist mission, while the aircraft hovered the medical corpsman or crew chief would use the hoist cable to lower a litter or harness to casualties below. The crew chief would sometimes lower a medical corpsman with the device. Then the hoist would raise both the medic and the casualty to the helicopter. The standard hoist could lift up to 270 kg (600 lb) in one load and could lower a harness or litter about 76 m (250 ft) below the aircraft. The only significant problem encountered by crew when they were using the hoist was that the helicopter became a sitting duck for enemy troops in the area while it was undertaking an extraction. In 1968, 35 aircraft were hit by hostile fire while on hoist missions and that number increased to 39 in 1969.

Vietnam veteran Phil Marshall was a member of the 237th Medical Detachment and flew unarmed MedEvac helicopters while in Camp Evans and Quang Tri. He arrived in Vietnam on 4 July 1969. During one mission he was hit in the arm by a bullet. He recounts:

'Serving as a medical "dustoff" pilot in Vietnam ranked near the top of dangerous assignments, starting with the conditions that the men encountered. We went out day or night, in all kinds of weather. We'd fly in the general direction of where the wounded were, but you're in the middle of the jungle and you have no landmarks. Soldiers set off smoke grenades so their rescuers could find them more easily, although the North Vietnamese tried to trick U.S. pilots by sending phony signals. They got $500 for shooting down an American helicopter, whether it had a Red Cross on it or not. Every second on the ground was an opportunity for the enemy to take us out.

'We almost crashed. The co-pilot took over, but then he froze on the controls. With no feeling in my hand, I grabbed the controls back. Then the co-pilot settled down and he flew us to the hospital with the wounded. Surgeries and recovery took about three months. I was supposed to receive a Distinguished Cross, but it never showed up. I did get a Purple Heart out of it.'

The term 'Dustoff' was coined in Vietnam, when it was chosen in 1963 from a codebook as the call sign for the 57th Medical Detachment. It evoked images of a Huey helicopter taking off from the dry and dusty Vietnam countryside and came to represent all MedEvac helicopter operations. The 57th Medical Detachment has the honour of being known as 'The Original Dustoff'.

Most air ambulances had qualified flight surgeons on board. They were physicians who had received formal training in the specialized field of aviation medicine. They were usually attached to an aviation brigade, which was in turn supported by a medical detachment team that provided dispensary service. When the situation allowed, triage and primary care for the wounded could be performed en route by the flight surgeons. The helicopter was indeed fast and efficient but it was also vulnerable to ground attack. Heavy bombers in World War II often flew missions that could take hours, but within the duration of the mission they would only be vulnerable to enemy fire for between ten and 20 minutes. In contrast, helicopters in

Vietnam were almost constantly exposed to hostile fire. This could even happen while they were in their base camps.

In 2017 Vietnam veteran nurse Lou Elsenbrandt recounted her memories of working under such challenging conditions:

'Within three months the chief nurse asked if I wanted the challenge of the emergency room. I accepted. After we cared for casualties we washed the blood down a drain in the concrete floor with a hose. Head injuries from rotor blades were the worse cases, horrible wounds. If a soldier was not ambulatory we utilized a gurney and used screens to block off a KIA or DOA. During triage if we determined a soldier wouldn't make it he was placed behind a screen then a nurse held his hand and talked to him until he died.

'One time after their village was hit, we had 99 Vietnamese civilians to care for within a 24-hour period. When wounded Vietnamese came in, so did the whole family. We also had Vietnamese nurses. They really helped due to culture differences.

'The realities of war? You try to forget them, but you never do. Every soldier brought into the emergency room had to have his fatigues cut from his body, fatigues frequently coated with Agent Orange. I recall the missing limbs, arms and legs dangling on shredded flesh, and one soldier we rolled over to check for exit wounds, his back stayed on the litter. We put him back down. He made it through surgery and we got him to Japan. Don't know if he made it or not. I think of that kid every day.

'You tried to be detached from the suffering, but I had an attachment to a young lieutenant who came in with his men. His unit took heavy casualties and he wanted to be with them, to see them through their ordeal. Next time it was him, peppered full of shrapnel. We were told he would lose both legs. That's one of the few times I had to walk out of the emergency room. It rattled me. We saved his legs, but I've seen him since returning home. His legs are not of much use; he's another boy I think about every day.'

The terrain may have been radically different but, like World War I, Vietnam was a war of attrition where each side chipped away relentlessly at each other's units. But success wasn't measured in territory gained; it was measured in body counts. Another similarity is in the many futile objectives it entailed, operations executed with courage, stoicism and discipline but often to little or no avail. Vietnamese hills and valleys paid for in American blood were frequently abandoned and dismissed without explanation. The problem wasn't the men in the field who fought like lions, it was the political machinations of corrupt governments and an openly biased media.

It is an irrefutable fact though that US casualties incurred in the Vietnam War received better and faster treatment than in any previous conflict. This was achieved because it was discovered early on in the war that relatively small numbers of helicopters had the capacity to evacuate larger numbers of patients to centrally located medical facilities much quicker than their predecessors. Technological advances propagated the improvement of effective radio communications, which factored into a greater ability to receive medical care using long-range radios known as PRC-25s that were able to cover distances of up to 8 km (5 miles). Moreover, the introduction of more powerful helicopters used as air ambulances far exceeded the capabilities of ground ambulances. The primary MedEvac helicopter in Vietnam was the UH-1 Huey, especially the UH1-D and the UH-1H, but others were also employed for this purpose. When a request was made for a rapid response for casualty evacuation, the air ambulance crews that scrambled had sufficient basic medical training to enable them to perform accurate triage and evaluate a patient's condition. They would then recommend the most suitable destination, and provide resuscitative care on the way. Such professionalism and dedication were unprecedented.

Vietnam presented extraordinary logistical challenges for the AEROVAC (Aeromedical Evacuation) system. This was primarily because of Vietnam's location in the tropical zone of Southeast Asia. There is a 12-hour time difference between Washington DC and Saigon. US military personnel arriving in Vietnam would need roughly four or five days to acclimatize to the significant time difference and to develop a fresh diurnal cycle. It also took two to three weeks to adapt to the heat and humidity of the tropics.

A total of approximately six weeks was required to develop a relative biological acclimatization to the types of infectious organisms that could be encountered in the new environment. Consequently, medical units stationed in Vietnam were compelled to develop better proficiency and a certain degree of autonomy, because the nearest offshore US hospital was almost 1,600 km (1,000 miles) away at Clark Air Force Base in the Philippines. These extended distances, even with modern air transport, demanded a nominal degree of self-sufficiency to be able to operate in the combat operation zones. The standard of qualifications and proficiency exceeded what had been required of medical staff in previous wars. During the Vietnam War the US military deployed a significantly higher ratio of medical-to-combat troops than had been used before in military operations.

Nurse Helen Eileen Hause served at 4162nd Air Force Hospital, 92nd Tactical Air Command Hospital, 6160th Air Force Hospital, 9th Aeromedical Evacuation Squadron, 820nd Medical Group and 81st Tactical Air Command Hospital. She recalled how they managed dealing with so many patients:

'I said to the chief nurse, you know, I'd like to go to Vietnam. And she said, "So would every other nurse." I said, Okay. She said, "Put your name on a list. The list is so long, you know, you don't have to worry about it." Well, I said, somebody must have burned the list, because three months later, I had my orders to go to Ton Son Nhut. We had an 85-bed staging unit. The army would bring in the wounded to the third field hospital, which was a big general hospital inside that, and take care of the guys, do their thing with them. And then they would bring them out to us. We would process them into the aerovac system. They would bring them in. We would keep them overnight, change their dressings, get them into pyjamas, give them baths, feed them, and then board them on the plane the next day.

'And sometimes they would come in from the MASH units ... These guys would still have the red clay of Vietnam on them, so we would, you know, do our thing with bathing and feeding and changing dressings. I just couldn't understand how humans could stand up to what those kids had just suffered and survived. It was amazing.

'We'd go to work 5:30 in the morning, and this other gal, who was a major at that time, she always wanted me to walk over with her. I'd walk over with her. We'd have to walk past the morgue. And I tell you, there is nothing to start your day than the smell of formaldehyde, and embalming fluid. So she would usually throw up on the way. I would just stop breathing until we got past that. And then we would get into the ward. And these kids, they would watch you when you were changing their dressings. They would read your faces. They would watch every movement, every expression on your face. So you just had to gear yourself just to not have any expressions on your face, and that was difficult. That was difficult. But that was the way it was.

'We had a six- or an eight-bed dispensary in connection with the eight- to five-bed casualty staging room. I thought [the other girl] was in charge of the whole place. We never… argued about that. I was her charge nurse, so we just got along fine. Not a problem at all. We were doing this six days a week. And we would work until the work was done, even though, you know, the schedule was three shifts. Everybody would just work until the work was done.'

Getting one's ticket back to 'The World' could depend on various factors. It was common practice for patients evacuated back to their home nation to be given a 'tour-completion' credit. This meant in effect that the casualty would not be required to return to active service in Vietnam. Originally, the policy just applied to battle wounded, but later on during the conflict this was extended to include those afflicted by disease and non-battle injury cases. In the autumn of 1965 the best way for a soldier to ensure being home with his family on Christmas was to contract malaria in the Highlands, or get seriously injured in a traffic accident. Even a bad 'accidental' burn could be your ticket.

Carolyn Hisako Tanaka was nicknamed 'Road Runner' for her unflagging energy and enthusiasm when she served in Vietnam. Of Japanese descent, at the age of six, she saw her family evicted from their California home in the wake of Pearl Harbor and relocated to an internment camp in Poston, Arizona. When the family returned to California after the war, they found their home burned to the ground. In 1966, she decided to enlist in the army as an emergency room nurse. Carolyn had the necessary skills and the ambition to do her duty for her country. Ironically, she returned from that war to a 'welcome' that evoked some bitter memories.

When Carolyn returned from Vietnam she was greeted with protestors and howls of derision. It reminded her of 7 December 1941. She wrote:

'This marks a very dark day in America's history, as well as for our family and that of 120,000 Japanese Americans living on the Pacific coast. WWII erupted and interrupted our family picnics forever. I was just going to turn 9 years old. By April 11, 1942, the "Yellow Peril" fever spread rapidly, and we Americans of Japanese decent could not be trusted by our government. Executive Order 9066 allowed the government to take us from our homes, strip us of our civil liberties and place us in internment camps all across the United States. Grandpa was taken without any notice of where he was going. He could only take the clothes he was wearing, a change of clothes and a toothbrush. The family learned he was sent to Bismark, North Dakota when he wrote asking for warm clothing to be sent to him. The family was not given time to sell our belongings or furnishings. Most of our belongings had to be given away to Mends or neighbors, including the elegant Boys and Girls Day doll sets. Dad wanted the family to go to the same camp as his sister, Aki, and mom's brother, Harvey. They were living in Dinuba with their four children. Dad found a house on the Wake farm. He took Hitoshi and me out of school and made plans to move us to Dinuba. Dad's oldest sister Toshi's husband was confined to a tuberculosis sanitarium, and unable to make arrangements for his wife and four children. They owned a produce market in Santa Maria. Dad made arrangements for them to move to Dinuba with us. Mother was due to deliver with her fourth child any day and could not travel. Dad had to stay behind with her. So the task of driving the family truck with all our belongings fell on the shoulders of dad's youngest sister, Sueko. She had not driven on the highway before on such a long journey. She was scared to death, but it was something that had to be done, and she did it. Many years later after her first tour of Vietnam she wrote, My trip home from Vietnam was a boring ride to Travis. In Oakland, five of us on the flight shared a cab ride to the San Francisco airport. We were advised to get out of uniform to avoid being spat upon or called "baby killers". We gave our blood, sweat, and tears for our brothers in combat, and this was the thanks we got.'

By the time the conflict came to an end there were over 5,000 American nurses working in Vietnam, with an average age of 23.6. Sixty-one per cent of all combatants killed were younger than 21, with 11,465 under 20. The average age of male fatalities was 23.1 years. Despite the use of the draft two-thirds of the men who served in Vietnam were volunteers and they accounted for approximately 70 per cent of those killed.

The last American troops departed Vietnam on 29 March 1973, and the fall of Saigon took place on 30 April 1975. Just for the record, it's important to point out that it was the South Vietnamese who lost the war, not the Americans.

CHAPTER SIXTEEN

IRAQ AND AFGHANISTAN

The immediate task allotted to allied army, navy and air force medical departments when they began to deploy to the Persian Gulf as part of a multinational effort called Operation Desert Shield was to provide this force with a full range of medical support. US diplomats immediately began pressing Saudi Arabia to admit American troops to deter possible further Iraqi aggression. Saudi Arabia was initially reluctant to invite Christians and female soldiers into a country that is revered by Muslims. Another item of contention was displaying the Red Cross on hospitals in a Muslim country, although this was quickly approved. The US 12th Evacuation Hospital, at that time located in Germany, would be the first hospital to deploy to the Middle East. The 12th was earmarked to support VII Corps, but at that time it was woefully unprepared. The unit had half its non-medical strength (administrative officers and non-medical enlisted personnel), but no actual medical personnel at their disposal. To compensate for this, the 7th MEDCOM drew on individual soldiers from other medical units and facilities in Europe. They even borrowed staff, including enlisted medical personnel such as pharmacy technicians, operating room technicians and licensed practical nurses, as well as maintenance personnel, especially senior non-commissioned officers and maintenance warrant officers.

General paranoia about the possible use of chemical weapons inspired Major General Michael Scotti, the commander of 7th MEDCOM, to initiate two particular training tasks for units preparing for deployment. The priority was how to handle the harsh desert environment without degrading their operations and, secondly, they had to fully prepare for the possible eventuality of Saddam's army using chemical WMDs (weapons of mass destruction). No WMDs were ever found in Iraq.

In the UK, the Gulf War action was codenamed Operation Granby. As part of this, on 22 September 1990 Field Hospital Aldershot deployed to Bahrain Island and then forward to Wadi Al Batin in northern Saudi Arabia. In October 1990, the staff of the Cambridge Military Hospital, Aldershot, were mobilized as 33 Field Hospital and sent to Al Jubayl on the east coast of Saudi Arabia. The Gulf War of August 1990 saw the largest deployment of the QAs (Queen Alexandra's Royal Army Nursing Corps) since World War II.

In preparation for the ensuing Operation Desert Storm US Air Force planes and Navy ships moved to the area, along with Marine Corps units that used equipment already in situ. Their challenge was to send a trained and equipped medical system more than 7,000 miles, to provide care for a population larger than that of Seattle, and dispersed over an area approximately one-fifth the size of the continental United States, and to prepare simultaneously for the expected continuous flow of mass casualties. Active US military physicians, dentists, nurses and other health care personnel from community hospitals and medical centres were quickly dispatched to serve in the battalions, brigades, divisions, ships, air wings, hospitals and field medical units being deployed to the Persian Gulf.

The Coalition's main logistics space was an area outside the port of Dhahran. For two weeks the main body of the 12th was stationed there in a tent city. This time was used practically to organize the unit and integrate the newly arrived medical staff with non-medical personnel. The chief nurse was obliged to meet all the new nurses, learn their qualifications and experience, and then assign them an appropriate position. Arriving equipment was unloaded, missing items were secured and transportation was arranged. It was game on.

At 3.00 am Baghdad time, on 17 January 1991, Operation Desert Storm was unleashed with the intention of driving Saddam Hussein's Iraqi forces from Kuwait. The precursor to Desert Storm beginning was an intense bombing campaign that devastated Iraq's infrastructure and destroyed many military supply lines. The air campaign was quickly followed by a ground war that lasted 100 hours, in which a vast international coalition led by 500,000 US troops routed the world's fourth largest army. The 'mother of all battles' predicted by Saddam Hussein didn't take long to deteriorate for the Iraq forces and become 'the mother of all retreats'.

In the wake of the terrorist attacks on the United States that occurred on 11 September 2001, US military forces were mobilized and deployed to Afghanistan in Operation Enduring Freedom (OEF) in 2001 and to Iraq in Operation Iraqi Freedom (OIF) in 2003. These forces had at their disposal highly trained and specialized army field medical units, such as the previously mentioned Mobile Army Surgical Hospital (MASH), the Combat Support Hospital (CSH) and the Forward Surgical Team (FST), as well as equivalents that accompanied Air Force and Navy units. These medical teams became almost immediately familiar with the types of casualties, both military and civilian, caused by insurgent guerrilla warfare. However, thanks to advances in both civilian and military medicine more soldiers are surviving grievous wounds than in previous conflicts.

By 2017, America, supported by the United Kingdom and other NATO allies, had been continuously involved in a war for the past 13 years. A total of about 2.5 million Americans have served in Iraq or Afghanistan at some point in the post-9/11 years, many of them more than once. The main distinction in these recent conflicts is that more women have assumed frontline combat duties than in any previous wars. The extent of female service members' involvement in OEF and OIF, in terms of both the number of women deployed and the scope of their involvement, is unprecedented. In 2010 the US Army Special Operations Command created a pilot programme to put women on the battlefield in Afghanistan, and in January 2016 the armed services lifted a controversial ban on women serving in positions of direct combat. Since then, women soldiers have patrolled the streets of Fallujah and Kandahar. They have driven in convoys on desert roads and mountain passes, they have deployed with Special Forces in Afghanistan on cultural support teams, they have scrambled into the cockpits of fighter jets and crawled out of the bloody rubble caused by IED explosions. They have become an integral part of all military operations.

One person who experienced Iraq first-hand was Corrine Lynn Schurz from Easton, Pennsylvania. Her account below of her combat experience has a very contemporary, candid feel to it and confronts one of the many issues facing today's military. Openly gay, she was eager to serve her country and learn a useful life skill, so she enlisted in the United States Army as a radiology specialist. She began training as a medical specialist (combat medic) and went on to become an X-ray specialist. After AIT (advanced individual training) she was stationed in West Germany. While there she earned the Expert Field Medical Badge and was promoted to Specialist 5. After returning to the United States she joined the US Army Reserve and spent the next 19 years as an actively drilling reservist in the numerous medical units that were staffed by the reservists drilling in Grand Rapids, Michigan, and ending with the 323rd Combat Support Hospital and the 322nd Medical Company based in Southfield, Michigan. During her time as a drilling reservist, Schurz was promoted to sergeant first class. She graduated from nursing school and was commissioned as a second lieutenant in June 2003.

Schurz deployed with the 325th Combat Support Hospital to COB Speicher, outside Tikrit, Iraq, where she served as a medical-surgical nurse caring for injured and sick Americans, Iraqis, coalition forces and third country nationals (working as contractors). A Combat Support Hospital (CSH) has the job of stabilizing the patient and providing specialized treatment within a combat zone. Patients who couldn't be returned to duty were evacuated to hospitals in US military bases in Europe. An active CSH provided up to 248 beds and was capable of providing general, orthopaedic, thoracic, vascular, urological and gynaecological surgery. The CSH has extensive laboratory capabilities: X-ray, ultrasound scan, CT scan, blood bank and physiotherapy.

While deployed Schurz received the Army Commendation Medal. She ended her 28-year military career honourably on 29 June 2008 as a result

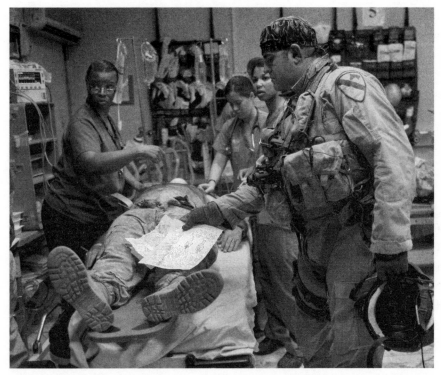

The mortality rate for those wounded in contemporary conflicts has decreased significantly thanks to units such as the Afghan 28th Combat Support Hospital in Iraq.

of President Clinton's 'Don't Ask, Don't Tell' (DADT) policy. This is the term commonly used for the policy restricting United States military personnel from efforts to discriminate or harass closeted homosexual or bisexual service members or applicants, while barring those who are openly gay, lesbian or bisexual from military service. Schurz lives with her loving partner and says:

> 'I am a lesbian and have always been a lesbian, and so part of it was which branch of service was less likely to care or toss me out because of being a lesbian. The Marines don't have a medical field, and that's where I wanted to go ... for a couple of reasons. One, I did not think that ... it was likely that the medical field would ask me to do things ... that violated my personal code of ethics.

'My duties were the following. I worked in the intermediate care ward on the night shift, so ... basically I was a medical/surgical nurse. We basically took care of anybody that was sick because medical stuff was sort of, medical assets were divided up ... So we took care of folks that were sick. There were soldiers that could go back to duty. We took care of folks that were injured, that way usually they got, if they were American they got Evac'd. If they were coalition forces they got Evac'd. We took care of third country nationals that were mostly working as contractors, and we took care of Iraqis, the police, the Army and civilians that got injured ... We did have a couple of mass casualties, so we got to take care of them. You know, war is pretty violent and doesn't make a lot of sense most of the time.

'I certainly have served with many women that have honored themselves, and many of them, certainly from my perspective, were lesbian, not all, and sexual orientation doesn't make a good or bad soldier one way or the other, whichever way we are in it, but clearly for my identity it's been important to find my sisters in common. I think that lesbians in the service haven't really been recognized because we, just as gay men, had to be under the radar. So, coming out to me is important in the process. So, since the Army had already gotten it, we're there.'

Almost 90 per cent of combat medics assigned with line units participated in combat patrols and most of those experienced some type of hostile incoming fire. Roughly a third witnessed someone from their unit or an ally being seriously wounded or killed, or enemy troops being seriously wounded or killed. The signature wounds of returning Iraq and Afghanistan war veterans are represented by the dual conditions of post-traumatic stress disorder (PTSD) and traumatic brain injury (TBI). Anger and aggression can be correlates of both conditions.

The military history of Afghanistan is a long and bitter legacy. Many historians have often referred to Afghanistan as the 'graveyard of empires'. Over 2,000 years ago Alexander the Great experienced the fighting in the northeast. For him and his army it was a long and bloody war of guerrilla actions and sieges, and Alexander would spend the better part of three exhausting years attempting to subjugate the recalcitrant peoples of the distant satrapies of the region. He would inevitably fail. The British invasion of 1839 initially produced a stunning victory for the imperial army, but this was quickly followed by a stunning defeat that was consequently followed by a second victory. In 1878, the British invaded again. Though they suffered a major defeat at Maiwand, their main army eventually defeated the Afghans. The British then re-drew the frontier of British India up to the Khyber Pass, and Afghanistan had to yield various frontier areas. The Afghans initiated the fighting in the third Anglo-Afghan war when Amanullah Khan sent troops into British India in 1919. Within a month they had been forced to retreat.

Contrary to popular belief, the Russians did not suffer a major military defeat in Afghanistan. Granted, the Afghan mujahideen won some important encounters, notably in the Panjshir valley, but they definitely lost others. The truth is that it culminated in a stalemate and neither side decisively defeated the other. The Soviets could have remained in Afghanistan for as long as they wished, but they decided to leave in 1988 when Mikhail Gorbachev estimated that the war had reached an impasse and was no longer viable in terms of the cost in men, money and international prestige.

The current conflict in Afghanistan began in 2001, in the wake of the catastrophic events of 9/11. The Bush administration's purpose was to eliminate the terrorist threat of al-Qaida leader Osama bin Laden. US forces initiated the War on Terror by attacking the Taliban, on the premise that they were hiding and protecting this wanted terrorist, the evil mastermind behind the attacks on the Twin Towers. The UN Security Council issued punitive sanctions against Afghanistan. These sanctions, along with the ensuing Afghanistan War, may have led to the Taliban's downfall but they were not eliminated. In late December 2014 the NATO combat mission ended and was replaced by an assistance mission baptized Resolute Support. The name of the mission or operation is largely superfluous to the casualties that are incurred, and with every war there are inevitably casualties. However, improvements in battlefield medicine means that more than 90 per cent of soldiers wounded in Afghanistan survive. That's a marked improvement on the Vietnam War's 86.5 per cent track record. It is estimated that the cost of veterans' medical and disability payments for the United States alone over the next 40 years could reach as high as $1 trillion. Considering that these young men and women are prepared to give everything for the country they served and suffered for, the personal cost to those who return dismembered and disfigured is incalculable.

Chantelle Taylor joined the British Army at the tender age of 22 in 1998 as a combat medical technician. She served in Kosovo, Sierra Leone, Iraq and Afghanistan. Almost 12 years after initial enlistment she was commended to take the Queen's commission from the ranks, but opted to leave the service instead. She returned to Afghanistan for a third time with the US Department of State, where she helped to develop the trauma assistant programme and completed two years as an instructor in combat medicine. Her contribution to the world of tactical medicine continues with her experiences in the field shared through the interactive soldier exhibition at the National Army Museum in London. Chantelle was formally presented to Queen Elizabeth II and Prince Philip during the official museum opening ceremony. Her military memoir *Battleworn*, along with her poem 'Keep me Awake', was featured as part of the British military's contribution to the Warrior Care exhibition of art in Washington DC in 2016.

A war, a conflict, a police action, an insurgency; all these descriptions are surplus to requirements to the medical teams patching up and reassembling the shattered bodies of young men and women wounded in action. Regardless of the nature or the reason for violent confrontation they are always required to do their job. In Vietnam nurses and doctors had to deal with injuries that resulted from bullets, bombs and booby traps, but during the Iraq and Afghan wars a new menace surfaced that became the cause of a significant percentage of all Allied wounded. In the second Iraq War IEDs, or improvised explosive devices, were used extensively against US-led invasion forces and by the end of 2007 they had become responsible for approximately 63 per cent of coalition deaths in Iraq.

Between 2001 and the end of 2014, NATO/ISAF coalition forces suffered 1,401 deaths as a result of IEDs, which is around 50.4 per cent of their total losses in combat. In the period from 2008 to 2011, IED fatalities amounted to between 58 per cent and 61 per cent of the coalition losses. The number of wounded from IEDs or the casualties among the Afghan forces aren't known, but according to data from the Pentagon's Joint IED Defeat Organization (JIEDDO) between half to two-thirds of Americans killed or wounded in combat in the Iraq and Afghanistan wars have been victims of IEDs planted in the ground, in vehicles or buildings, or worn as suicide vests, or loaded into suicide vehicles.

The IEDs are assembled using a variety of components that include an initiator, switch, main charge, power source and a container. IEDs may be surrounded by or packed with additional materials or 'enhancements' such as nails, glass, or metal fragments designed to increase the amount of shrapnel propelled by the explosion. Enhancements may also include other elements such as hazardous materials. An IED can be initiated by a variety of methods depending on the intended target. They were originally introduced to the Middle East and Central Asia, somewhat paradoxically, by the US military. Iraq insurgents probably learned how to manufacture the deadly devices from the electronically accessible US Army Technical Manual TM 31-210. They hurriedly improved on the basic American recipes, building a succession of harder-to-detect, more potent and easier-to-use contraptions. Iraqi know-how was successfully transferred to Afghanistan and continuously enhanced, both technically and tactically, thus turning IEDs into one of the most effective weapons in the armouries of the Taliban. The main issue with IEDs is that they are a weapon that doesn't only hit foreign troops on ground patrols and in road convoys; an IED is also an indiscriminate terror weapon that kills and maims thousands of civilians.

Treating casualties resulting from contact with IEDs presents new problems for medical teams operating in warzones. Due to its nature and mechanism, an IED has the potential to inflict a multidimensional injury, impairing numerous systems and organs. IED blasts can cause serious permanent or long-lasting disabilities that can result in amputations, internal injuries, burns, brain injury and psychological trauma. Even though victim-activated IEDs have a higher fatality rate than factory-made antipersonnel mines, as reported in Afghanistan, they still wound far more people than they kill, and most who survive these explosions will require medical and, in some cases, psychological assistance for many years to come. Victim-activated IEDs are devices that are detonated by the presence, proximity, or contact of a person or a vehicle.

IEDs are the source of the greatest fear that preoccupies most soldiers entering a warzone. The fear of losing a limb is one thing, but the fear of losing their reproductive organs is greater. The initial blast from an IED has the capacity to sever arms and legs, ripping through soft flesh, crushing organs and bone, and driving dirt, rocks and filth deep into gaping wounds. It can also mutilate the victim's genitals or blow them off completely. Knowing that he was earmarked for active duty in Afghanistan, one young, newly married marine planned to take the precaution of having his sperm frozen so that in the event of contact with an IED he and his wife would still be able to have children. Sadly, time constraints prevented him from doing this. A few weeks later he was on a combat patrol in Sangin, southern Afghanistan, walking behind an engineer sweeping for IEDs. There was a blinding flash, followed by a wave of searing heat. The upward blast ripped off both of the young man's legs and most of his left arm, slashing into his remaining arm, shattering his pelvis and driving a rock and other debris up into his abdominal cavity. Amid the bloody carnage, all the skin was ripped from his penis and his testicles were gone. Later, while recovering in hospital, he called his wife to apologize for the nature of his injuries. Holding back the tears she stoically reassured the wounded soldier and said, 'We will pull through this together, as a team.'

Despite some of the devastating injuries that occurred to soldiers in the field one particular unit, the British 34 Field Hospital at Camp Bastion, claimed a 98 per cent survival rate for casualties, making it a world leader in trauma care. Nevertheless, during a standard tour in Afghanistan there were reports that doctors and nurses, ambulance drivers and paramedics, hospitals and health centres all came under attack at some time or another. This naturally disrupted the delivery of medical care when needed most. Both civilians and combatants died because they were prevented from receiving necessary care on many occasions.

Physical wounds were one aspect, but psychological trauma or PTSD was entirely another. Michelle Partington left the RAF in 2015 after serving

20 years as a frontline paramedic. She was the first female paramedic to go to the frontline with the RAF Regiment and was operationally deployed on various tours with the MERT (Medical Emergency Response Team), taking emergency lifesaving care to the injured. She has worked in the UK and overseas in some of the most remote and austere environments. She joined the RAF in 1991 as an LAC, and reached the rank of sergeant before being commissioned as a medical support officer, providing tactical and strategic support for the Defence Medical Services. Michelle was a key part of building a paramedic cadre within the RAF and became the PTSD expert officer. She began writing a blog to help the public understand the mind of someone who suffers from PTSD. Writing about her experiences has been difficult but ultimately cathartic. She explains:

'One of the aircrew chaps came into the crew room to inform us we had a cab change. This was always a delight for us... NOT!!! It was all hands on deck to move everything from one Chinook onto another because the previous one had received a shot after being fired on during the last shout. I'm glad I hadn't noticed this whilst out on the ground. There is always a risk these days for sure, too many thumbs-down shouts. So, we carried out the cab change as quickly as possible and secured everything. Normally we are protected from a job during these cab swaps but we try to carry it out quickly because it meant we couldn't provide medical cover available for the guys on the ground.

'Unfortunately, the padre turned into a jinx because the radio shot into life "MERT & MERT FP you have an urgent MedEvac, acknowledge over." Anouska grabbed the radio and we ran leaving the padre to finish the film. We ran the couple of hundred meters to the cab, which used to turn into a race with FP, and donned our kit whilst the aircrew started up the Chinny. We were called out to 2 casualties who had received frag wounds, one of them to the head, which was not looking that great. My casualty appeared to be ok but you cannot take any risk because you don't know where the frag has gone. We have been called out to frag wounds in the past which we thought had been pretty minor but as we neared landing the patient went off on us due to a piece of shrapnel severing an artery. The fragments were made up of allsorts including bolts, basically anything the insurgents could find to cause damage. Thankfully the patients remained fairly stable throughout the flight back and on handover to the hospital.

'Normally following a shout the lead paramedic of the day and the doctor or nurse would transit with the patients to the hospital for handover, whilst the rest of the team and the aircrew return for refuelling and to replenish the medical consumables we had used. However, on this occasion there was no time to retrieve replacement med kit because as we pulled up to the Chinook we received a further call out. The doctor and I jumped out of the wagon dragging the oxygen with me as well as my osprey which was blooming heavy!! It was a rush and I was gagging for a drink. Thankfully we had a box on the Chinook with spare consumables for cases such as this so we dived into that for replacement kit. There was also water on the cab but it was warm and not very palatable. In fact, I cannot face drinking water now since serving in Afghanistan.

'The second call was to a single patient, one of our own lads who had obtained a head injury due to the weapon on his land rover spinning and hitting him. He was pretty stable and when we landed Anouska and I left the cab to escort him into ED. During the drive back to the cab we received a radio message from FP informing us we had yet another cab change. I couldn't believe it, what were the chances! As we approached the Chinook they were still midway through the cab change. I was about to jump out of the back of the land rover when I heard the dulcet tones "MERT & MERT FP you have an urgent medevac, acknowledge over." I turned to Anouska and said "We are in the middle of a f*****g cab change, give us a break!!" I was absolutely shattered and now wasn't feeling too great. Apart from this we hadn't had chance to drink or eat anything. Although we are normally protected from shouts during a cab change it transpired pretty quickly that it was a mass casualty situation so it was all hands on deck. So, we rushed the cab change, had yet again no time for a kit replenish and didn't have time to secure the kit as we had to take off. Apparently, they had 13 stretcher patients, 4-5 had passed away and various walking wounded. All the casualties were Afghans who had been in a market place when a suicide bomber arrived. Some of the 13 were extremely critical and included a child already in cardiac arrest.

"I wasn't looking forward to getting off the ground to assist further but I had to. The US Pedros had commenced the triage as they had arrived on scene first. MERT was known for having the most clinical expertise due to having an anaesthetist etc. on board whereas the Pedros did not. The team initially thought we would be taking the stretcher patients due to the fact we had the expertise on the cab and could hold more patients than the Pedros who could only carry 2 stretchers. However, it soon became apparent that 3 of the casualties had life threatening head injuries and needed to go direct to Kandahar if they were to stand any chance of survival.

The Medical Emergency Response Team treat an IED casualty in Helmand Province, Afghanistan.

Our Chinook was the only airframe, which had the reach to make the journey so we took them. I settled my patient to the stage where only routine observations were required. I checked the rest of the team and they did not require further assistance. I struggled to try not to be sick and my head was banging. At one point I had to stand up because I was about to vomit all over my patient. That would really not have been a good day for that patient at all. It was so funny during the flight because as you may recall we hadn't had enough time to secure the kit before we left. Well, although it shouldn't be funny the spinal board kind of slipped and almost fell on Brian. I'm still smiling about it now, sorry Brian! I was so relieved to be landing in Kandahar but when I looked out there wasn't an ambulance in sight. I was fuming, maybe a bit too unhappy but it had been a very long run of shouts. We couldn't really wait around so I had to run about 300 metres in full body armour and helmet to reach the ambulance guys and tell them we need the patients taking off the helicopter.

'Finally, we dropped the patients into the hospital and made our way back to the flight line to await the return of the Chinook from refuelling. I felt so ill and I just couldn't keep it in anymore and vomited there and then!!!'

Michelle continues to be an inspiration to other PTSD sufferers. In 2017 she participated in the wonderful Invictus Games in the rowing and powerlifting disciplines, and it's a trend she is determined to continue.

One of the most disturbing aspects to emerge from recent conflicts comes as a result of social media. Soldiers go on patrol wearing head cams that have live-streaming capabilities and many carry mobile phones. Some of these recordings end up both inadvertently and purposely on social media, where many quickly go viral. During the raid on Osama Bin Laden's compound by US Navy Seals, live video footage was allegedly streamed to the White House.

A helmet camera recorded an incident in 2013 that led to the conviction of a British Royal Marine for murder, for the shooting of an unarmed and injured Afghan insurgent. Military authorities regarded the act as being in contravention of the Geneva Convention. The audio and video images were used in evidence at a court martial relating to the incident. Insurgent groups such as so-called Islamic State have been quick to weaponize social media for their own nefarious designs, and these days they use every available platform in a no-holds-barred policy for the purpose of recruitment and disseminating evil propaganda.

CHAPTER SEVENTEEN

WHERE DO WE GO FROM HERE?

The experiences of World Wars I and II provided significant advances in battlefield medicine. In World War I, approximately four of every 100 wounded men who received treatment could be expected to survive; in World War II that figure rose to 50 of every 100. Closer examination of historical casualty rates indicates that almost 50 per cent of military personnel that were killed in action died as a result of excessive blood loss. Eighty per cent of those succumbed within an hour after initial injury. To a combat medic those first crucial 60 minutes are known as the 'golden hour'. If the surgeon, nurse or combat medic can treat the hemorrhage within an hour after the initial injury has occurred, the wounded have a far greater chance of survival. For the past two decades combat medics have trained intensively to keep wounded soldiers alive while bullets and bombs are being exchanged, on the reliable assumption that assistance is always just a radio call away, and these days it usually is.

Combat medics still fulfil a bipartisan role when serving on the frontlines. They are expected to be trained soldiers and fight alongside their brothers and sisters in arms, but they are also tasked with preserving life on and off the battlefield. They are expected to be both warrior and healer. But it's important to remember that these remarkable individuals are not automatons; they are living, breathing human beings who suffer the same stresses and anxieties as the other soldiers they serve with. They are indeed courageous and tenacious but they are not invulnerable and consequently many suffer from residual post-traumatic stress symptomatology. Despite being revered and considered irrepressible by their peers, they are often deeply affected by their combat experiences. The compulsion to internalize traumatic experiences is heavier among combat medics, but there are inevitably consequences.

Their double-duty role subjects combat medics to stress factors that other military specialties are sometimes oblivious to. The task of continually providing frontline aid means that some are potentially at high risk of burnout, compassion fatigue, combat stress and PTSD. The symptoms often rely on trigger factors, events or occasions that cause the sufferer to relive the initial trauma, which can result in feeling on edge, nightmares or abnormal sleep patterns. These stress reactions are common after a traumatic event and in many cases they may subside after a couple of months; however, medics with PTSD can experience a whole plethora of related symptoms even years after the event occurs.

This was the case with volunteer nurse Augusta Chiwy, who wasn't a combat medic, just a civilian nurse who inadvertently found herself saving lives on the frontline. Seventy years after the events that impacted her life during the Battle of the Bulge she couldn't hear the name 'Bastogne' without becoming traumatized.

Like other war veterans, many former medics experience depression, anxiety, marital problems and substance abuse. Those experiencing the effects of PTSD are often inclined to self-medicate with alcohol, prescription medication or illegal drugs, and in many cases the symptoms don't dissipate with time. Being a combat medic doesn't make one exempt from the dangers of being on the frontline. If anything it exacerbates them. They are not doctors and are perfectly capable of disposing of an enemy combatant when required, which makes them fair game for the opposing forces. If a medic is tending a wounded soldier it's safe to assume that they are already in a precarious situation and prone to enemy fire.

Despite the fact that throughout recent decades there have been gargantuan strides made in the advancement of treating chronic and debilitating disease processes, traumatic injuries sustained during active service continue to represent an impracticable balance between basic physiology and time.

Relying on immediate tourniquet utilization, stabilization by Forward Surgical Teams and prompt evacuation of the wounded to higher levels of care has enabled frontline units to increase individual survival rates to a factor of 90 per cent. In some cases when the wounded person was able to make it to a higher level of care the survival rate was as high as 97 per cent.

Talented military commanders always respected the terrain where their armies fought and the really good ones often used geographical features to their advantage. Prior knowledge of the terrain and environment will inevitably impact how medical services are deployed to support the troops in action, because these variable environments will present unique challenges for those providing battlefield first aid.

To deal with emerging weapon technologies, advance medical-care requirements need to develop congruently at the same rate. This will inevitably present challenges because diverse terrains will require different approaches. Fighting in an urban environment is significantly different than having to negotiate a mountainous battlefield. Distinguishing the needs for various environments will be a critical element in maintaining future readiness.

Modern medical teams and combat medics are trained to deal with the deleterious effects of repetitive strain injuries and heat exhaustion, and have identified the initial steps in the management of head injuries and urgent limb preservation. Sophisticated algorithms for the care and recovery of the severely injured soldier have advanced throughout the last decade and military medicine continues to innovate.

Maybe the future will see the use and deployment of artificial intelligence in the shape of autonomous systems capable of guiding providers of various skillsets or even directly providing care to the wounded? Modern technology and growth in the understanding of biological processes offers tremendous opportunities to combat the scale and magnitude of battlefield medicine's challenges. A futuristic battle suit with a network that can connect an injured troop with doctors at a hospital potentially thousands of miles away is already being developed. The battle suits are embedded with technology that can track the troop's location, vital signs and even administer medicine to reduce shock. The information means a combat rescue officer will be able to begin conducting triage even before physically arriving on the scene.

There was a relatively recent case of a healthy 22-year-old male soldier who suffered severe blast injuries to the torso after the nearby detonation of an IED. He was immediately put on a MedEvac helicopter and placed under the auspices of flight medic for transport to the nearest military surgical hospital, which was roughly 50 km (30 miles) away. Once the wounded soldier was secured inside the helicopter, intravenous drips were applied and he was given analgesia as the helicopter exited the combat zone under enemy fire. During the wound assessment the soldier's vital signs registered normal, but after several minutes in transit he began to complain of severe abdominal and chest pain. The flight medic requested more details, but the soldier's utterances were becoming increasingly unintelligible. Moreover, the situation was exacerbated due to the clamorous engine noises of the helicopter.

Within moments the soldier became progressively tachycardic. His oxygen saturation began to deteriorate and his heart rate began to rise. The flight medic performed an e-FAST examination with a portable ultrasound device. The e-FAST examination provided an ability to assess for life-threatening injuries during evacuation. His abdominal and pericardial ultrasonographic windows were negative for the presence of intra-peritoneal or pericardial fluid. As the patient's vital signs continued to deteriorate, ultrasound imaging of the thoracic fields revealed the presence of a large right-sided pneumothorax. Right pleural-space needle decompression, followed by placement of right-sided tube thoracostomy, placed to suction, was immediately performed, with the resulting normalization of all vital signs. The soldier's life was saved thanks to modern technology.

Despite the introduction of these technologies, contemporary combat medics will still be compelled to prove their efficiency in four major competencies before deploying to the frontlines. Emergency care, evacuation, medical force protection and limited primary care will remain the core knowledge skill of all combat medics. Emergency care implies the accustomed skills of combat casualty care and trauma resuscitation. Specific skills include haemorrhage control, splinting, bandaging, advanced airway management, intravenous fluid therapy, decompression of tension pneumothorax and shock management.

Gender is no longer an issue on the front lines as shown here with this Combat Support Hospital nurse in Iraq.

One US combat medic recently said:

'I've noticed over the past 18 years how much the equipment we use has improved but in my opinion it still comes down to training. When I first began training as a medic, to stop bleeding it was always about applying pressure and elevating and in the worst-case scenario you apply a tourniquet. After being at war for a few years our bosses told us to use the tourniquet right away because that saves more lives.

'The evolution occurred over 4 to 6 years; it was a case of "Hey look this seems to work better so let's do it. It's saving more lives on the battlefield so let's do this and train accordingly." So, we went from training our guys on the ground, from applying pressure and elevating to "hey put the tourniquet on immediately to stop the bleeding because you want to save a life instead of just prevent damage." The triage process became a little more streamlined, a little easier. It's not just the medic that's doing this on the battlefield. The medic is doing the triage, whether it be a medic or a nurse or a doctor or someone who is medically qualified. But you also have other people around who can manage this and they may not be medical personnel but they have the basic training that we call "Combat lifesaver training" in the US Army, to be able to sustain life. Maybe it's not immediate but then we have something we call a battle buddy who can also apply a tourniquet if there's massive bleeding, and they can apply a chest feel or something like that, and that's kind of how it evolved. Sometimes you feel like you're never prepared enough because what we do is so important, we try and take care of casualties the best we can. But unfortunately not all of them can be saved you know, then you always have this feeling of inadequacy, what could I have done better to save this person's life. I never felt when I had a casualty that there was something that I forgot to do or something that I knew how to do that I didn't do. It was always, I wish I would have known how to take care of this person better, or would it have helped or would it have made a difference.

'The way I see things evolving is there are a lot of new products that people are coming out with, that after their experiences on the battlefield or experiences themselves. They're coming out with better ways to stop the bleeding because that's the most important, or being able to get them back to a higher echelon of care. The way I see a thing evolving is, way back in the day, back before this war started, medics in the military were trained to do all your basic stuff … They know how to stop bleeding, they know how to give oxygen and they know how to do CPR. It's becoming more advanced now to where they realize the initial point of care when the person was first hit, you know the "Golden hour" is the most critical. In order to maximize that time, when there is no way you can get someone off the battlefield and into a higher echelon of care. Investing more money and more training into individuals. Each individual that is there, and not only investing in the knowledge of the medic that's on the ground but investing in the knowledge of every person around because 9 times out of 10 there's only 1 medic for 20, 35 people. But if everybody knows basic care then they can provide aid until the medic is able to do what they can do.

'As far as advancement is concerned, there may be a few technological advancements, things like that, maybe some new equipment. But I think that the biggest thing that they'll start doing is start investing in the knowledge and the capabilities and allowing the medics on the ground to do more. They already do it with Special Forces Teams and other high efficient teams but they're also going to begin in giving a higher degree of medical knowledge to all the other medics who are on the ground. Being able to transfer that knowledge to everybody else in the platoon is equally important, so that they can help out when they can.'

Military planners have long envisaged using robotics on the battlefield, and the potential for utilizing parallel technologies suitably developed to enhance the practice of battlefield medicine and trauma care in the future is also in the pipeline. The future may see remote-controlled automatons proliferating in ground medical operations, where they will have the potential to reduce casualties among combat medics, and significantly improve the life-saving effectiveness of medical interventions, while in the process further reducing battlefield mortality rates.

As contemporary military planners prepare for contingencies involving operations by sizeable forces for special operations and conflict situations, which may involve a limited military intervention force, the archetypical linear battlefield situation we have known in the past will become antiquated. The potential for new high-tech weaponry, use of chemical and biological agents, along with combatting non-traditional forces and terrorism will demand a totally different approach to deal with what will be perceived as a 360 degree threat.

The general consensus of opinion among the military hierarchy is that the increasing global urbanization of the world's population implies that it's more than likely that future battles will be fought within city limits. Cutting-edge advanced technology may indeed pave the way for enhanced combat casualty care, but it will not entirely eliminate the need for human intervention. The combat medics will still carry tourniquets, junctional haemorrhage control devices and intraosseous needles (used for injecting directly into the marrow of a bone).

Despite all the advances, many of these so-called new tools and concepts have existed in some form or another for centuries, and history should never forget the innovators. Such is the nature of humanity that it's practically inevitable that there will always be wars and conflicts, and combatants in harm's way may get wounded. As long as that is the case, the ultimate purpose was, is, and will remain, despite whatever technology is used, the optimization of care on the battlefield, and caring, like courage, cannot be programmed into any machine.

Bibliography

William Allan. *Homer: The Iliad* (Bristol Classical Press, 2012).

William Beatty. *The Death of Lord Nelson.* (CreateSpace Independent Publishing Platform, 2015).

Nathan Davis. *History of Medicine: With the Code of Medical Ethics* (Applewood Books, 2010).

Horatio Gates. *The Horatio Gates papers, 1726-1828.*

J. C. Goddard. 'Genitourinary medicine and surgery in Nelson's navy', *Postgraduate Medical Journal*, 81 (2005).

Roger-Henri Guerrand and Fernande de Bissy. *Oeuvres D'Ambroise Paré* (4 vols.). (Union Latine d'Editions, 1976).

Dr William Hanson, M.D. *Smart Medicine: How the Changing Role of Doctors Will Revolutionize Health Care.* (Palgrave Macmillan, 2011).

Philip K. Hitti (tr.) *An Arab-Syrian Gentleman and Warrior in the Period of the Crusades; Memoirs of Usāmah ibn-Munqidh.* (New York, 1929).

Woody Holton. *Abigail Adams, Biography & Autobiography* (Tantor Media, Inc., 2009).

Lucy Hutchinson. *Memoirs of the life of Colonel Hutchinson* (Longman, Hurst, Rees and Orme, 1806).

Martin King. *Searching for Augusta: The Forgotten Angel of Bastogne* (Lyons Press, 2017)

Martin King and Michael Collins. *Voices of the Bulge: Untold Stories from Veterans of the Battle of the Bulge* (Voyageur Press, 2010)

J. Kirkpatrick & I. L. Naylor. 'The qualities and conduct of an English surgeon in 1446: as described in a manuscript attributed to Thomas

Morstede'. *Annals of the Royal College of Surgeons in England*, 79:3 (May 1997).

Oxford Dictionary of National Biography, entries on John Bradmore and Thomas Morstede. (Oxford University Press, 2004).

Ellen Newbold La Motte. *The Backwash of War: The Human Wreckage of the Battlefield as Witnessed by an American Hospital Nurse* (G.P. Putnam and Sons, 1916).

Dominique Jean Larrey. *Memoirs of Military Surgery, and Campaigns of the French Armies* (Classics of Surgery Library, 1985).

A. Louis. 'Excerpts from the eulogy of Jean-Louis Petit presented during the public session of the Royal Academy of Surgery on May 26, 1750.' *Annals de Chirurgie* 126:5 (June 2001).

Stanley F. Malamed. *Sedation: A Guide to Patient Management* (Elsevier, 2017).

National Maritime Museum, Greenwich, London. 'Journal of the HMS *Vanguard*, 1797 by John Grimshaw'.

Daniel Nijensohn. 'Admiral Horatio Lord Nelson's Death at the Battle of Trafalgar: A Neurosurgeon's Forensic Medical Analysis.' *Journal of Trauma & Treatment*, 6:2 (2017).

Ambroise Paré. *La Méthode de traicter les playes faictes par hacquebutes et aultres bastons à feu* (1545).

Ambroise Paré, (tr. Robert White Linker and Nathan Womack). *Ten Books of Surgery: With the Magazine of the Instruments Necessary for it.* (University of Georgia Press, 1969).

Michelle Partington. Author communications and questions.

Pope Gregory I. *Dialogo de sam Gregorio*. (Presso l'Accademia della Crusca, 1979).

Diane Purkiss. *The English Civil War. Papists, Gentlewomen, Soldiers, and Witchfinders in the Birth of Modern Britain.* (Basic Books, 2009).

Bernard D. Rostker. *Providing for the Casualties of War: The American Experience Through World War II.* (RAND Corporation, 2013).

Stanley G. Schultz. 'William Harvey and the Circulation of the Blood: The Birth of a Scientific Revolution and Modern Physiology', *Physiology* 17:5 (October 2002).

Corrine Lynn Schurz Collection, Veterans History Project

(AFC/2001/001/97568, Library of Congress, 2001).

Walter Simons. *Cities of Ladies: Beguine Communities in the Medieval Low Countries, 1200-1565*. (University of Pennsylvania Press, 2003).

P. Skandalakis et al., '"To Afford the Wounded Speedy Assistance": Dominique Jean Larrey and Napoleon.' *World Journal of Surgery*, 30:8 (July 2006).

Peter Stanley. *For Fear of Pain: British Surgery, 1790-1850*. (Editions Rodopi, 2003).

Mabel Keaton Staupers. *No Time for Prejudice* (Macmillan, 1961).

Julia Stimson. *Finding Themselves: The Letters of an American Army Chief Nurse in the British Hospital in France* (Macmillan, 1918).

Morris Stockhammer. *Plato Dictionary* (Philosophical Library, 2015).

Carolyn Hisako Tanaka. "Memoir, Road Runner" by (unpublished manuscript, Library of Congress, 2001).

The National Archives of the UK. 'Journal of HMS *Captain*; by James Farquhar, Surgeon; between 3 September 1798 and 26 May 1799.' ADM 101/93/2D.

The Nursing Mirror and Midwives Journal (1915–1918).

Marie-Cécile Thoral (tr. Godfrey Rodgers). *From Valmy to Waterloo, 1792-1815* (Palgrave Macmillan, 2011).

Vegetius (tr. Lieutenant John Clarke) *The Military Institutions of the Romas (De Re Militari)* (1767).

Andreas Vesalius. *De humani corporis fabrica libri septem* (1543).

Index

Picture Credits

Alamy: 89 (GL Archive), 245 (Harvey O. Stowe)

Bridgeman Images: 21

Getty Images: 165 (ullstein bild), 190 (Bettmann), 211 (Interim Archives), 214 (Bettmann), 216 (Bettmann), 229 (John Moore/Staff), 237 (Marco Di Lauro/Stringer)

Library of Congress: 100, 111

Metropolitan Museum of Art: 18

National Archives and Records Administration, US: 132, 207

National Library of Medicine, US: 57, 65, 102

Public Domain: 29, 30, 33, 46, 53, 70, 83, 116, 127, 129, 141, 159, 162, 168, 183, 189, 192, 197

Shutterstock: 31

Wellcome Collection: 40, 43, 50, 63, 67, 76, 93, 151, 173, 182